CRYSTALS

SYMMETRY IN THE MINERAL KINGDOM

With an introduction by Vincenzo De Michele

CRESCENT BOOKS

Contents

5 The meaning of 'crystal'
What is a crystal?
7 Symmetry and symbolism
8 The shapes of crystals
10 Crystallographic indices
12 The seven systems
Cubic system
13 Hexagonal system
Trigonal system
14 Tetragonal system
Orthorhombic system
Monoclinic system
Triclinic system
Development of crystals
Twinning
15 Aggregates
Regular growth of crystals

All photographs by Carlo Bevilacqua

Translated from the Italian of Vincenzo De Michele

Printed in Italy by IGDA, Novara
Library of Congress Catalog Card No: 70-188867

Crystallography is a science as complicated as it is little known to the public, who usually regard it, on the basis of prejudices picked up at school, as a minor and somewhat disagreeable subject. It is, moreover, a science with its roots in mineralogy, physics and chemistry; none of them easy to explain to the uninitiated reader to whom these pages are addressed.

Our intention is not to describe the whole of crystallography, nor to present a complete exposition of the laws which determine the formation of crystals. The purpose of this book is to explain, as simply as possible, some of the more obvious properties of crystals, so that the reader may more easily understand the mineral world and its fundamental crystal structure.

It has seemed important to me to lay stress on the geometric symmetry of crystals and on the laws of Haüy, basing my approach above all on the experience and results of an elementary course which I once gave to young collectors. The short glossary included in the section on massive and microcrystalline mineral forms is a modest attempt to assist the reader to grasp the morphological nomenclature which has been adopted in descriptive mineralogy. The text, illustrated by numerous drawings derived from the original publications, is only an introduction to the magnificent photographs specially taken for this book in the Natural History Museum of Milan by Carlo Bevilacqua. My sincere thanks are due to the director of this museum, Prof Cesare Conci, for his help and encouragement.

Vincenzo De Michele
Natural History Museum, Milan

The meaning of 'crystal'

In common parlance the word crystal is used to describe those products of the glass-making industry which are noted for their transparency, purity and brilliance; and, by extension, the adjective crystalline is applied, for example, to water of exceptional clarity, or to a pure and precise literary style. 'Crystal' is a term of perfection, which conjures up for us the slim and precise proportions of transparent quartz, or rock crystal. No doubt this mineral, which can be found in all parts of the world, caught the imagination of men in very ancient times; and they would have valued it as highly for its remarkable regularity of form as for its transparency.

It was the Greeks who gave the mineral its name of *krystallos*, which literally means 'frozen ice', because they believed it to be water frozen by intense cold; and this belief survived into medieval times. No doubt the remote sources of this product of nature, mysteriously manufactured in high and almost inaccessible places, encouraged this belief that crystal was quartz which had taken on the properties of ice. As Pliny recorded in his *Natural History*: 'crystal is only found in those high places where the winter snows have gathered in great quantity, and it is surely ice; and for this reason the Greeks have given it its name.' And when he writes of the crystal *sexangulum*, he obviously means prismatic quartz with its hexagonal cross-section, the most common form in which this mineral occurs.

Since the two obvious characteristics of crystal were transparency and geometric regularity, all minerals which possessed these two properties must be forms of crystal; so the word came to be applied in a way which still holds good. Today, however, we know something more: it is the structure of the substance, the way in which its external faces are shaped and related to one another, which defines it as a crystal. Look, for instance, at a piece of common granite through a lens: the particles of which it is made up are compressed chaotically together, and it is neither transparent nor geometrically regular; and yet each of those individual particles is as perfect a crystal as any of the superb examples to be found in a museum, or in the photographs in this book.

What is a crystal?

Two simple experiments help us to understand the most important characteristics of the crystalline state.

Take a vessel full of water, and heat it until it boils: it begins to boil at a temperature of 100°C, and it remains at this temperature until all the water has boiled away. The water has been converted from its liquid state into a gaseous state, as steam, and this occurs exactly at 100°C. If, instead, the water is cooled until it freezes, it begins to turn into crystalline ice at 0°C exactly; and if ice is melted again into water the temperature will remain at 0°C until all the ice is melted.

Now take a thin rod of glass: the flame of a candle or a match should be sufficient to soften it. As the temperature is raised the glass gradually softens, melting into a more and more liquid form. There is no fixed melting point, and the substance is slowly converted from a solid into a liquid form.

These differences of behaviour are due to differences in the way the atoms are assembled in the structure of the substances. The atoms which make up all matter are not motionless and rigidly fixed; they are in constant motion, and the energy they possess, and which they reveal in movement, increases with the temperature. In a solid, such as a metal, the atoms move relatively small amounts about an equilibrium position (see figure 1a); as the solid melts, they move more, slipping and sliding against one another with greater freedom, but without completely losing their original relationship one with another. This is the liquid state (figure 1b).

If the temperature is raised still further, the substance breaks up into individual molecules (made up of only a few atoms), or even into individual atoms; this is the gaseous state (figure 1c).

Obviously, as the substance is cooled down, it should be

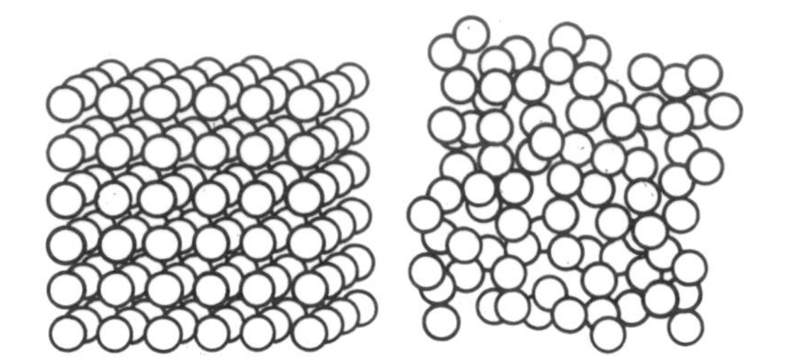
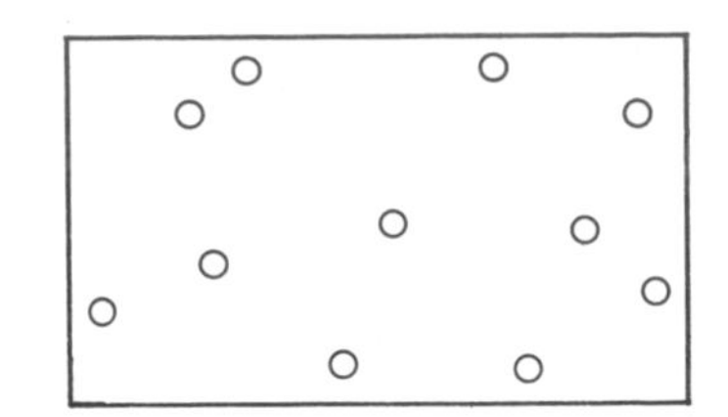

Figure 1

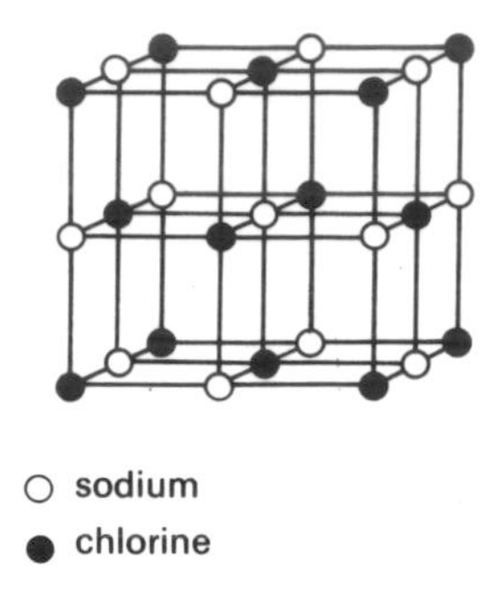

Figure 2

possible to lower the temperature sufficiently to reach a point at which the atoms and molecules are completely without movement; this is the definition of the so-called 'absolute zero', which is around −273°C.

Now let us look again at the solid state, as it begins to form when a liquid is gradually cooled. As the temperature falls, the atoms begin to arrange themselves in an ordered structure, evenly distributed in relation to one another; they are separated by regular intervals, although these are not necessarily the same along each of the three spatial dimensions.

In the solid state of sodium chloride, common salt (figure 2), each atom of sodium is surrounded by six atoms of chlorine; and, conversely, each atom of chlorine is surrounded by six atoms of sodium. It is this regularity of structure which gives a crystal of salt its transparency and its cubic shape; and in fact the solid state is synonymous with the crystalline state. A substance such as glass is not truly a solid: it is a liquid which has cooled so much that its atoms are almost motionless, but they are still disordered in relation to each other, a condition which is characteristic of the liquid state. Substances such as this, which do not have a fixed melting point but gradually soften and become more liquid, are said to be 'amorphous' (without shape).

The study of crystals was begun by the Dane Niels Stensen in 1669, and continued by Guglielmini (1655–1710). Their work was formulated in 1772 by Romé de l'Isle into a physical law: 'In all crystals of the same substance the angles between corresponding faces have the same value (when measured at the same temperature).'

But the 'father of crystallography' was the son of a poor French weaver, René-Just Haüy. He was educated as a botanist; but one day, when he had accidentally dropped and broken some calcite crystals, he noticed that the smallest fragments all had identically shaped crystal faces. From this he concluded that crystals were built up from a large number of tiny units, all of which had the same shape, and which he called integrant molecules. In treatises published in 1784 and 1801 he developed his theory, proposing three basic types of integrant molecule, which could be assembled into a crystal much as a builder assembles bricks into a house; and so introduced the concept of the discontinuous structure of crystals.

Researches pursued during the nineteenth century helped to define this concept better. The three integrant molecules proposed by Haüy proved insufficient to explain the structure of all known crystals. The inspired idea of the crystal 'house' built from innumerable crystal 'bricks' was completed by Bravais, who worked out mathematically the number of different-shaped bricks that could exist. These bricks, or space lattices, are defined by lines joining the centre points of adjacent identical atoms, as in the representation of sodium chloride (figure 2). Altogether there are 14 distinguishable Bravais lattices, and these can be grouped, according to shape, into seven systems.

The next major step in crystallography came when the German scientist Max von Laue suggested the use of crystals in his experiments to determine the nature of X-rays. If crystallographers were correct in their insistence that crystals were discontinuous in their nature, and consisted of a network of dense points separated by regular fixed distances from one another, then it would be expected that X-rays passing through a crystal would be scattered in a regular pattern. The experiment, performed in 1912, was an important event in the fields both of physics and of crystallography: the diffraction pattern produced when X-rays passed through a crystal of zinc sulphide confirmed the wave nature of the radiation, and also showed that crystals possessed a latticed structure of the postulated kind. This work was followed up by W. H. Bragg and his son W. L. Bragg, who established the science of X-ray crystallography with their determination, in 1913, of the structure of sodium chloride.

From that point, researches into the structure of crystals have made great strides, and have been of particular importance in the study of minerals. It has

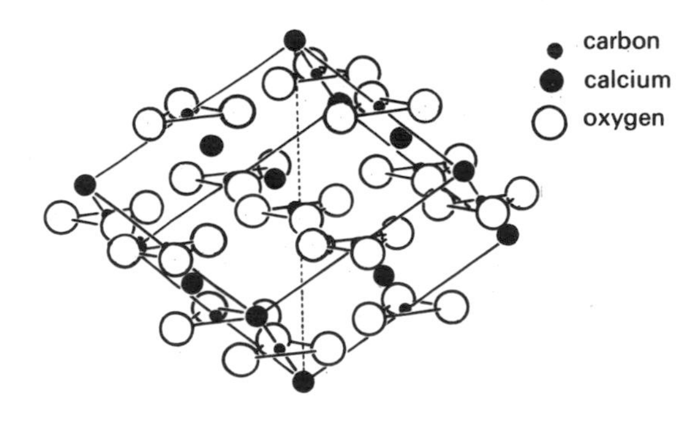

Figure 3

been shown, in fact, that all minerals crystallise with their own individual structure, with characteristic unit cells. A unit cell is the smallest possible spatial unit which can possess all the physical, chemical and geometrical characteristics of the mineral as a whole.

Figure 3 represents the unit cell of calcite, crystalline calcium carbonate, which belongs to the crystal system known as trigonal or rhombohedral: the atoms of calcium are situated at the corners and in the centre of each face of the cell, while the carbonate groups, consisting of three oxygen atoms around an atom of carbon, occupy the middle of each edge of the cell. The dotted line represents one of the axes of symmetry of the crystal: that is, rotation of the crystal about this axis will reveal the same configuration of crystal faces three times during the course of a single rotation.

In practice, crystallography has almost completely abandoned the study of morphology, in as much as the form of the crystal is a direct outcome of its internal structure; nevertheless, a short introduction to some aspects of crystals which are geometrical rather than physical can help us to a better understanding of minerals in general.

Symmetry and symbolism

We cannot lose sight of the fact that crystals are, above all else, solids of relatively simple geometrical form and with a remarkable regularity of faces, angles, etc; but there is no reason to suppose that all geometrical forms will occur in nature. Among known crystals, for instance, there is no prism with a pentagonal or heptagonal base.

All crystals have symmetry. For instance, any crystal can be rotated about a number of different axes in such a way that the same configuration of faces appears more than once during the course of rotation: these are axes of symmetry. There are planes of symmetry, along which it would be possible to cut a crystal in half, so that each half was a mirror image of the other; and there is a centre of symmetry, so that every face of the crystal has a similar face lying parallel to it on the other side of the crystal.

The human body, for instance, shows symmetry; this is bilateral symmetry, so that all the elements that make up the left side are repeated on the right side: eyes, ears, hands, legs and so on. It is as if half the body were reflected in a mirror cutting through it, and the mirror is situated in the plane of symmetry.

The geometrical operation is very simple: given a point situated in a given position before a plane of symmetry, one measures the perpendicular distance from the point to the plane, continues the measurement for an equal distance on the other side of the plane, and there establishes the mirror image of the original point.

Consider now an infinite number of points, constituting a plane parallel to the plane of symmetry and extending to infinity; the mirror image would be another plane, parallel to the first, and also extending to infinity. These two planes would constitute the two faces of the crystallographic form known as a pinacoid.

Returning to the animal world for a moment, let us look at a five-branched starfish. If the five arms were identical, we could turn the animal on its base in such a way that we could not distinguish which of the five arms was pointing toward us. Here we have symmetry with respect to an axis which emerges vertically through the centre of the animal. This is five-fold symmetry, since five times in a rotation of 360° the animal has an identical appearance; but in crystals, for reasons which we shall see later, five-fold symmetry does not occur.

Now we will consider again the cubic form of a crystal such as sodium chloride; this form also occurs in many other common minerals, such as galena (lead sulphide), fluorite (calcium fluoride) and pyrite (iron sulphide). Through the centre of each opposite pair of faces we can imagine an axis emerging (figure 4); as the cube is rotated about each axis, each of four faces will appear in turn, with a rotation of 90° to bring the cube into a position where it is indistinguishable from its previous position. Each axis has four-fold symmetry, and the

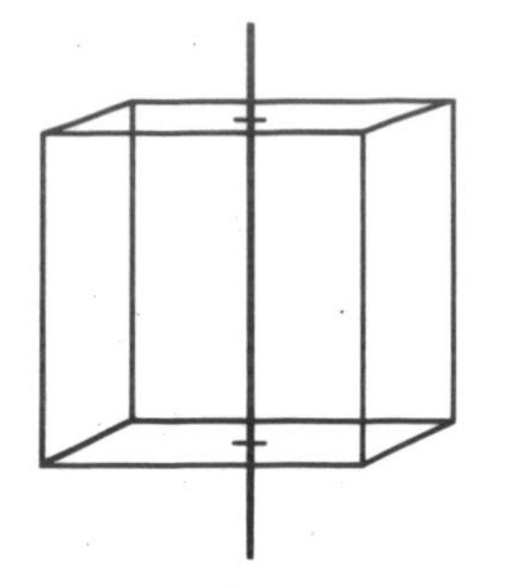

Figure 4

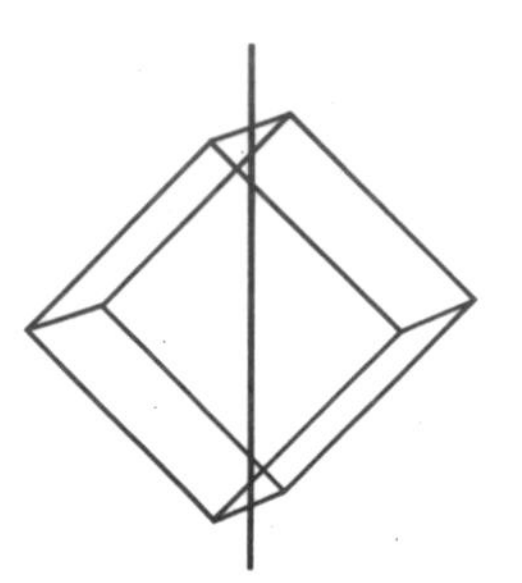

Figure 5

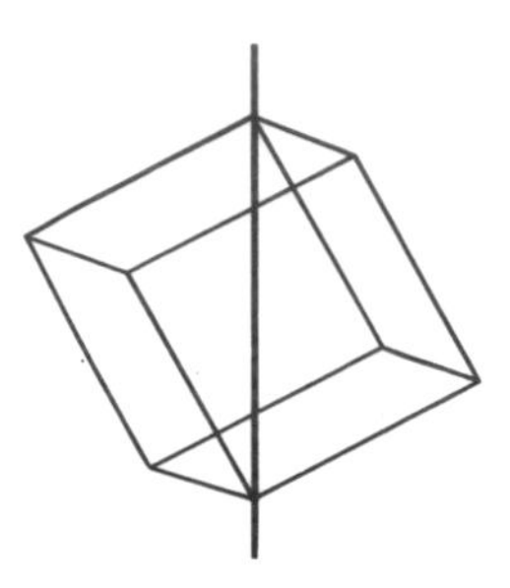

Figure 6

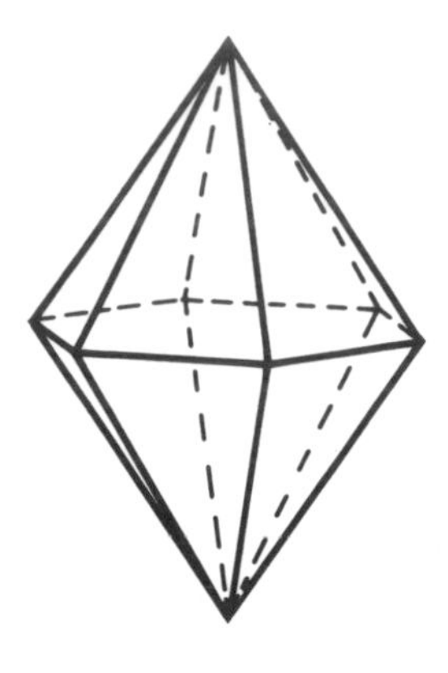

Figure 7

three axes are known as tetrad axes.

Where the six faces of the cube meet, they form 12 edges. Through each pair of edges opposite to one another we can imagine another axis (figure 5). Such an axis is two-fold in its symmetry, or diad, since the same configuration occurs only twice during a complete rotation. There are six of these diad axes in a cube.

Each cube also has eight corners, and rotation axes can be imagined passing through each opposite pair of corners (figure 6). There are three upper inclined faces, and three lower; as the cube is rotated, each of the three faces is brought into the same position, and therefore these axes have three-fold symmetry. There are four of these triad axes.

Now let us consider any one of these axes in abstract, together with a plane parallel to it and isolated in space. If the axis is diad, symmetry will give us another plane parallel to the first, and forming a pinacoid analogous to that we have already obtained in the case of a plane of symmetry. A triad axis will give us three planes, meeting one another at an angle of 120°; in theory they extend to infinity, but in practice they are limited on two sides where they each intersect with one another, and only extend to infinity in the directions parallel to the axis. This form, like a triangular box open at both ends, is called a triangular prism; and the open form can be closed by a pinacoid, a bipyramid, a rhombohedron, etc. In the same way, tetrad and hexad axes can generate tetragonal and hexagonal prisms.

If the plane is not parallel to the diad axis of symmetry, but inclined toward it, the form generated is a dome, very similar to the roof of a house. Triad, tetrad and hexad axes generate respectively trigonal, tetragonal and hexagonal pyramids.

As for the centre of symmetry, it will lie at the point of intersection of axes or planes of symmetry: in a cube, for example, the opposite faces, sides and corners are all symmetrical with respect to a centre of symmetry, and the same is true of tetragonal and hexagonal prisms.

The presence of one or more elements of symmetry and their various combinations will produce all the forms of crystals. For example, a hexad axis with a plane of symmetry perpendicular to it will generate, with an inclined face, a hexagonal bipyramid whose six upper faces are due to the hexad axis, and whose six lower faces are the reflection of the six upper faces in the plane (figure 7).

As early as 1830, J. F. C. Hessel was able to predict that the various symmetry elements could be combined in 32 different ways, giving rise to the 32 classes of crystal symmetry. But, as we have seen in figure 3, certain groups of atoms form definite shapes within the crystal lattice, and so have a symmetry of their own. In all, there are 230 possible internal arrangements of this kind, and these are known as space groups.

We have already pointed out above that five-fold symmetry does not exist in the crystal world; neither does seven- or eight-fold, or any higher number. All crystals possess either diad, triad, tetrad or hexad symmetry, and to understand why, we must go back to the idea of space lattices as building bricks.

We have seen that these bricks exemplify the three physical characteristics of crystals: homogeneity, periodicity and discontinuity. In figure 8, a number of identical bricks have been fitted together in a schematic representation of a crystal structure; only 8a–d and 8f give structures which are completely homogeneous, and without interstices. Moreover, it is only in these structures that periodicity is maintained: that is, every lattice point is always the same distance from the next. The structures which cannot fulfil all necessary requirements are those with five-fold, seven-fold and eight-fold axes.

The shapes of crystals

Looking at the shape of some typical minerals, we can begin to understand the way in which the world of crystals is divided into seven lattice systems.

For instance, in some solid forms such as the cube, octahedron or rhombic dodecahedron, the edges are all

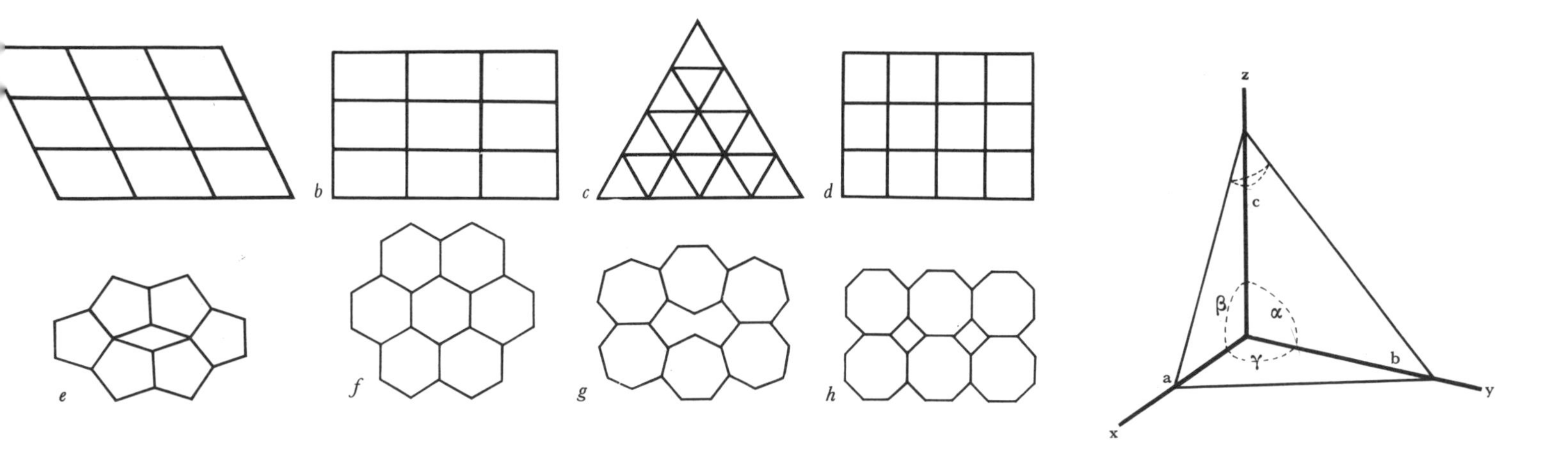

Figure 8

Figure 9

of the same length. In crystals of these shapes, as well as in the pentagonal dodecahedron, the hexakisoctahedron and the diakisdodecahedron, there is no preferred direction in which the crystal has grown. Minerals of equal size in each dimension include pyrite, fluorite, galena, diamond and garnet.

Other minerals, such as beryl or apatite, occur in the form of prisms of hexagonal section; while phosgenite, cassiterite and vesuvianite are four-sided prisms. Here the preferred direction of growth of the crystal is clearly along its length; while the four or six sides are of equal length, and at equal angles of 90° and 120° respectively.

The crystals of topaz, barite and celestine are also prisms, and with one dimension developed more than the others; but their section is a rhomb whose two diagonals, of different lengths, represent the other two dimensions.

Crystals of another group of minerals which includes gypsum, crocoite and orthoclase, are also prismatic in form; but in this case it is as if the prism had been distorted along its length in a characteristic way. Finally, the crystals of minerals such as axinite or rhodonite have edges which are all of different lengths, and which meet at different angles.

All the minerals which belong to a particular crystal system possess a common fundamental characteristic which can be summed up in a geometrical figure representing the greatest possible symmetry of the system. Alternatively, we can define a set of three axes, similar to cartesian axes, but which are defined by the three dimensions of the crystal. Three axes are chosen which are those of the geometrical form that best represents the symmetry of the system: the cube, tetragonal prism, etc.

The Bravais space lattices can be arranged according to their shape into seven systems. Of the fourteen possible shapes, three are cubic; that is, they have edges of the same length which meet at right angles. Two more lattices are similar, except that one set of edges is different in length from the other. The first three lattices are classified in the cubic system; the second two in the tetragonal system.

Four more lattices have their edges still at right angles to one another, but all three sets of edges are of different lengths; these make up the orthorhombic system. In the monoclinic system there are two lattices in which two sets of edges are inclined to one another, but are both at right angles to the third. There is only one triclinic lattice, in which all sets of edges are unequal in length, and are inclined to each other at three different angles.

This leaves two Bravais lattices. The hexagonal lattice would appear at first to belong to the orthorhombic system, but it is a particular prismatic form with a rhomboid base with an angle of 120°. Three lattices of this form combined will give a hexagonal prism. The final lattice has the shape of a rhombohedron; it is known as the trigonal lattice.

The three directions of the Bravais lattices define the three crystallographic axes of the crystal, and it is usual to imagine the origin of these axes at the centre of the crystal, extending in the direction of the edges of the lattice forward and back, up and down, and from side to side. In figure 9 these are seen as the x, y and z axes respectively; the angles between them are α, β and γ as shown in the diagram.

In the cubic system the three axes are orthogonal (at right angles), and because lattice points will be repeated at equal distance along all three, the axes are described as being of equal length. The tetragonal and orthorhombic systems also have axes which are orthogonal; but in the tetragonal system the z axis is longer than the other two, being also an axis of tetrad symmetry; while in the orthorhombic system all three axes are of different length.

All three axes of the monoclinic system are unequal. The angles between the x and y, and the y and z axes are right angles; but the z axis is inclined away from the x axis, making the β angle greater than 90°. And in the triclinic system, the axes, as well as being of unequal length, are inclined to one another at different angles.

The principal use of these crystallographic axes is in naming and defining the various crystal faces that can be

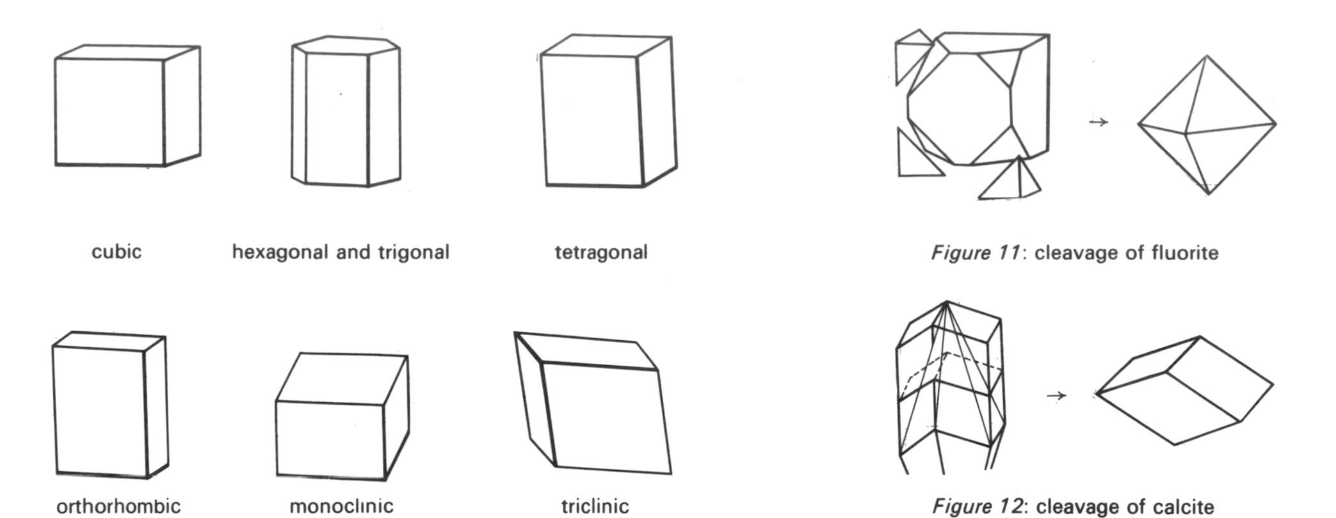

Figure 10

Figure 11: cleavage of fluorite

Figure 12: cleavage of calcite

formed, and in the case of the hexagonal and trigonal systems it becomes necessary to define a fourth axis. Three axes of equal length are parallel to the hexagonal edges of the Bravais lattice and in a horizontal plane; they are at 120° to each other and are called the *x, y* and *u* axes; the *z* axis is at right angles to all three, and is of greater length. In terms of these axes, there is no difference between the trigonal and hexagonal systems; in terms of symmetry, the difference lies in the fact that the *z* axis is triad in the trigonal system, and hexad in the hexagonal system.

Crystallographic indices

In the same way that a point on the earth's surface can be defined accurately when we know the geographical co-ordinates of its latitude and longitude, so we know the position of a crystal face and its orientation with respect to the others by the use of three (or, in the case of the trigonal and hexagonal systems, four) crystallographic indices. The faces of a crystal are directly related to one another and to the atomic structure: any face which is formed corresponds to a plane that is particularly rich in the dense points which represent the central positions of the atoms. The denser such a plane is, the more easily a crystal face will be formed there, and the more easily the crystal will cleave along this plane revealing a characteristic form.

Credit is due to Haüy for having first appreciated the relationship between the various faces of crystals, and for having attributed this to their structure. Fascinated by the phenomenon of cleavage, which had already attracted the attention of other scientists, Haüy obtained many specimens from various private collections on which to carry out his observations. He found that, in certain transparent crystals like calcite, fluorite and gypsum, it was possible to observe in them a series of fracture lines parallel to each other; often there was more than one series, each at a different orientation. When the mineral specimens were broken up, they divided into smaller solids with faces corresponding to these fracture lines. This characteristic of crystals is now well understood, since we know their atomic structure: cleavage is produced along planes where there is relatively high density of atoms, and where there is low cohesion between parallel planes. Fluorite, for instance, produces cleavage fragments which have the faces of an octahedron (figure 11); in calcite (figure 12), the cleavage follows a rhombohedron, in galena and rock salt a cube, and in gypsum the easiest cleavage follows a pinacoid, giving rise to characteristic plates. In mica, where the cleavage planes are only a few atoms thick, the well-known flakes are produced by what is known as basal cleavage.

Haüy took a prism-shaped crystal of calcite and continued to reduce it by cleavage until he obtained a rhombohedron, as shown in figure 13. When he took other shapes of calcite crystal, such as a scalenohedron, he always finally obtained the characteristic rhombohedral form by cleavage. And from this rhombohedron he obtained eight times by successive cleavage a smaller rhombohedron, until finally it was too small to be seen. It was from this that he deduced that all crystals were made up of a very large number of tiny polyhedric bodies, which could be combined in various ways to give all known forms.

The other, and erroneous, part of Haüy's theory reduces the primitive forms of crystals to five, each in their turn made up of three types of integrant molecule. By the addition or subtraction of rows or sheets of molecules, Haüy showed that it was possible to obtain all the forms then known; for instance, by removing successive molecules from the corners of a cube he obtained an octahedron, while by removing them from the edges he obtained a rhombic dodecahedron. Beginning from whatever crystal form, all others could be obtained by the addition or subtraction of an integral number of layers of molecules; given one face, the others could be obtained by appropriate means.

To return now to consideration of the crystallographic

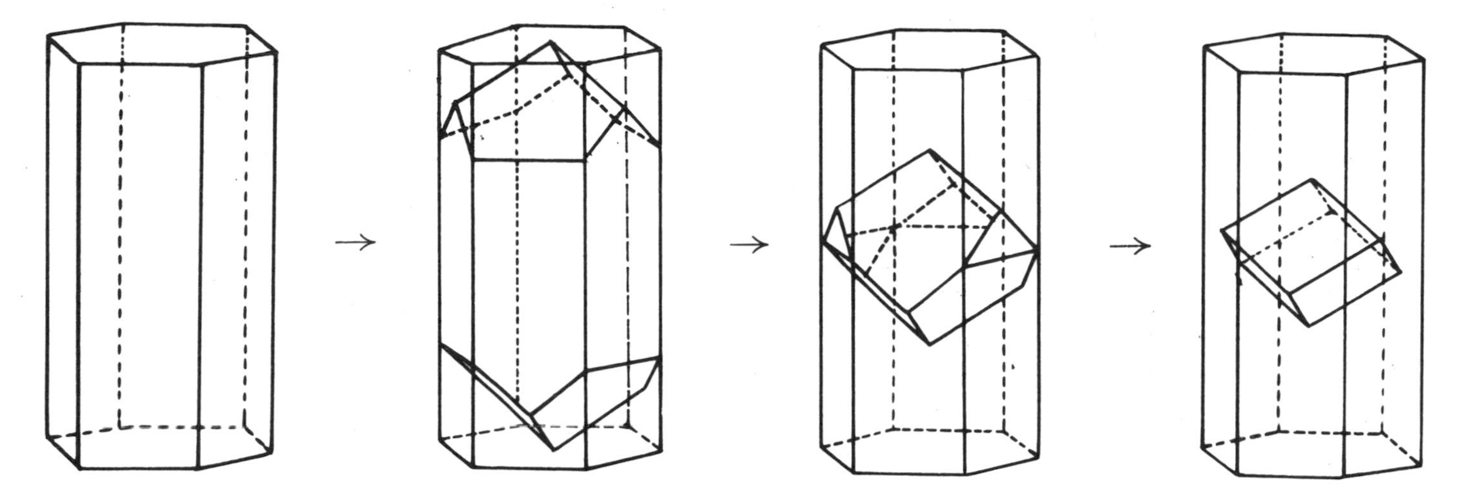

Figure 13

indices: let us consider three axes at right angles to one another, and a plane (representing a crystal face) which intersects one or more of these axes. We shall know the inclination of this plane, and its orientation in space, when we know the relative distance from the origin at which it intersects each axis. Such a distance is called a parameter. For instance, if a crystal face is well inclined toward the z axis, it will intersect it only a short distance from the origin, and its z parameter will be small, while its x and y parameters will be large. On the other hand, a nearly vertical face will have a z parameter which is nearly infinite. So, to know the spatial position assumed by any face, it is sufficient to know its parameters with respect to the crystallographic axes.

In defining the spatial orientation of any face, however, it is not necessary that the parameters should be measurements of real distances from the origin. Suppose that the face intersects the x axis at a distance a, the y axis at a distance b, and the z axis at a distance c; we can identify this face by the ratio of these three distances – $a{:}b{:}c$. These are known as Weiss indices, after the system devised by C. S. Weiss; but the more commonly used indices are those devised by the nineteenth-century British crystallographer W. H. Miller. These Miller indices are the reciprocal of the Weiss indices.

Suppose for instance that $a = \frac{1}{2}c$, $b = \frac{1}{3}c$: then the Miller indices are obtained as follows:

$$\frac{c}{\frac{1}{2}c} : \frac{c}{\frac{1}{3}c} : \frac{c}{c} = 2{:}3{:}1$$

This is written in the symbolic form (231). A face that cuts each axis at an equal distance from the origin will have the indices (111); a face that cuts the x and y axes at an equal distance, but is parallel to the z axis, will have the indices (110). This is because its intercept on the z axis will occur at infinity, and the reciprocal of infinity is zero. Other sets of indices for different faces are given in figure 14; and it will be noticed that an intersection on an axis in a direction away from the observer is given a negative index, in the form $\bar{1}$.

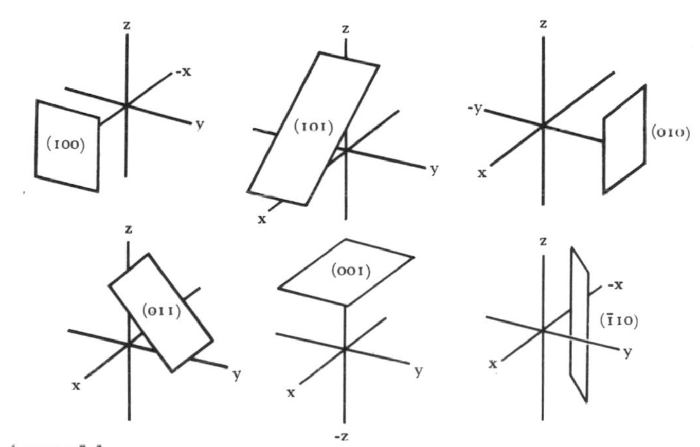

Figure 14

These indices do not provide a physical measurement of the position of a face, but only define its orientation in space. This is shown in figure 15, where it is obvious that an infinite number of parallel faces, all with the same Miller indices, can exist at any distance from the origin.

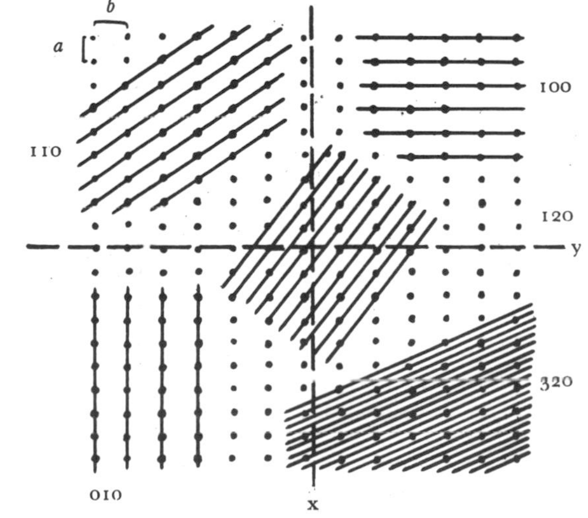

Figure 15

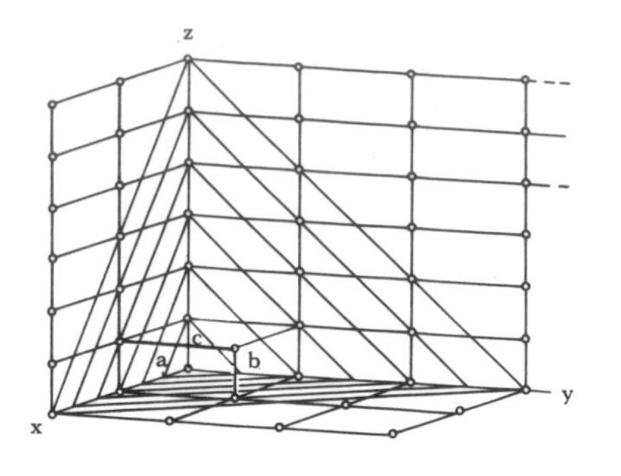

Figure 16

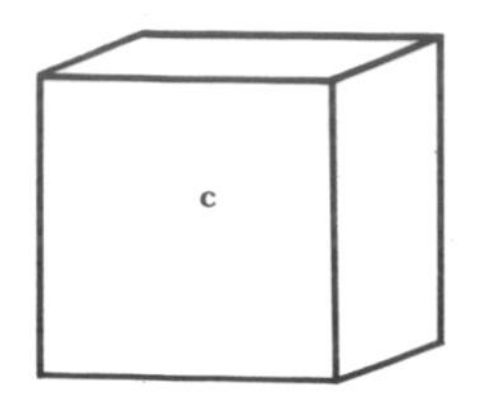

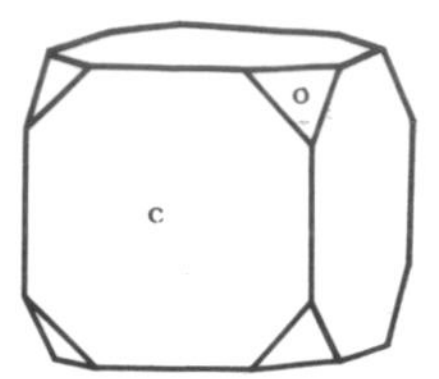

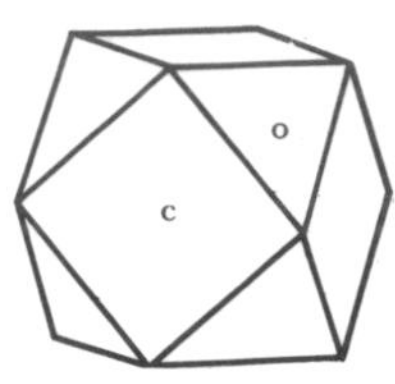

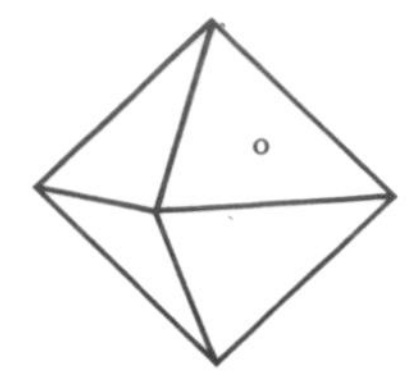

Figure 17: from cube to octahedron (cube face *c*, octahedron face *o*)

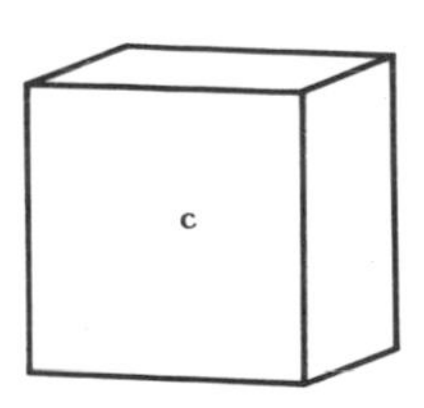

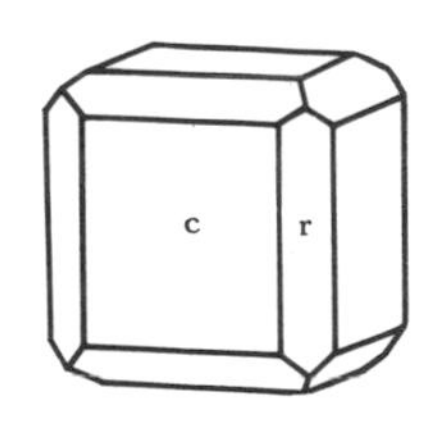

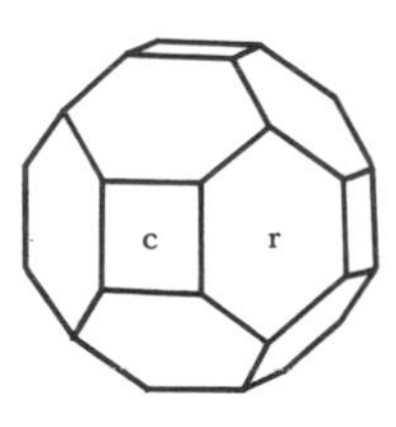

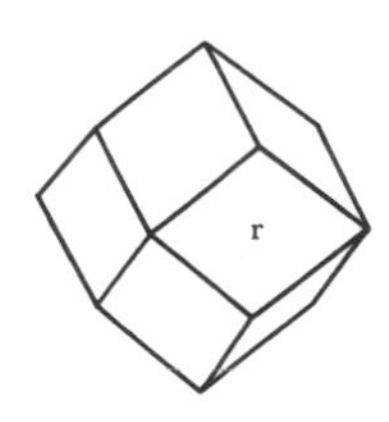

Figure 18: from cube to rhombic dodecahedron (faces *c* and *r* respectively)

It was a matter of observation on the part of Haüy that the orientation of crystal faces was such that their intercepts on crystal axes were always rational (that is, they could be stated in terms of simple fractions, which would always give simple whole numbers for the Miller indices). This led to the formulation of the law of rational indices. It should be noted that in the case of the hexagonal/trigonal systems, which have four axes, the Miller indices consist of four figures.

When it is considered that the position of crystal faces is defined by the lattice points, and that the lattice points mark the central positions of the atoms making up the crystal, it is at first remarkable that the dimensions of the lattice should be related by such simple ratios. Miller indices are seldom greater than 3, although indices as high as 6 are known. Figure 16 shows a hypothetical crystal with lattice points at the corners of a unit with sides *a, b,* and *c*; a series of parallel planes of indices (321) intersect the axes as shown. It is clear that, the lower the Miller indices, the greater the number of lattice points each plane will contain. Preferred crystal faces, therefore, will have low Miller indices.

Each crystalline system possesses a number of elements of symmetry, the number diminishing step by step as one goes from the cubic to the triclinic system. Thus one can progress from the holosymmetric class of the cubic system – holosymmetric meaning the class which has the greatest number of elements of symmetry compatible with the lattice – to the pedial class of the triclinic. The cubic holosymmetric class is represented by the hexakisoctahedron, which has three tetrad axes, four triad axes, six diad axes, nine planes of symmetry and a centre of symmetry; the triclinic pedial class is totally asymmetric, each face being a different shape, or pedion. Modern crystal morphology employs a special notation for each class of symmetry, which is beyond the scope of the present work. Nevertheless it is worthwhile noting that a face of known indices associated with one or more symmetry elements creates in space a geometric form, which may be either open or closed, which is identified by the same indices, but placed in brackets of a differing type.

Considering the cubic system, for example: if we take the fundamental face (111), which intersects the three crystallographic axes at equal distance from the origin, then the other seven faces of an octahedron will have the indices $(\bar{1}11)$, $(\bar{1}\bar{1}1)$, $(\bar{1}\bar{1}\bar{1})$, $(1\bar{1}1)$, $(11\bar{1})$, $(\bar{1}1\bar{1})$, $(1\bar{1}\bar{1})$; and the form symbol for the octahedron can be simply represented as $\{111\}$. A form that makes a different intercept on all three axes is given the symbol $\{hkl\}$; if we consider the face (hkl) we obtain the 48-faced hexakisoctahedron, which is nevertheless still part of the cubic system: it can be regarded as an octahedron with six faces raised on each octahedral face. If one reduces the symmetry elements to four triad axes, three diad axes and six planes, the face (111) gives one a solid of four faces, the tetrahedron $\{111\}$.

Crystals seldom occur in these simple forms, but in a combination of forms. In such combinations, the respective faces frequently have the same size and appearance, which is an aid to identification; in the combination of cube and octahedron, for example, the six faces of the cube and the eight faces of the octahedron will show the same development. The shape of this kind of crystal is known as its habit: a cubic habit in the case of a crystal of fluorite (figure 17b) in which the corners of the cube are cut off by small faces which derive from an octahedron; a prismatic habit in quartz terminating in a pseudopyramid; a tetrahedral habit in zinc blende, which also reveals a cube; and a rhombic dodecahedral habit in garnets, in which one can also observe small icositetrahedral faces.

The most important forms of the various systems are listed below.

The seven systems

CUBIC SYSTEM. This system, whose symmetry we have already considered, comprises only closed forms. The principal forms, some of which are illustrated in

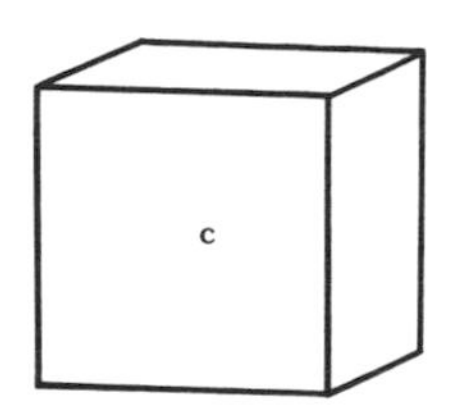

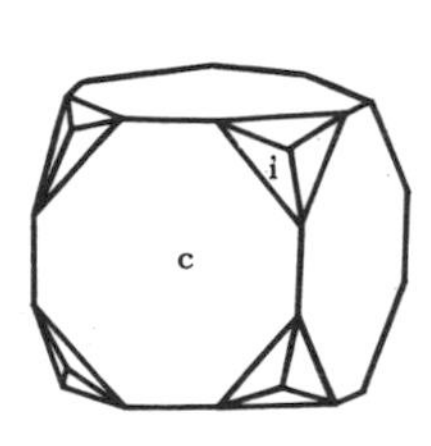

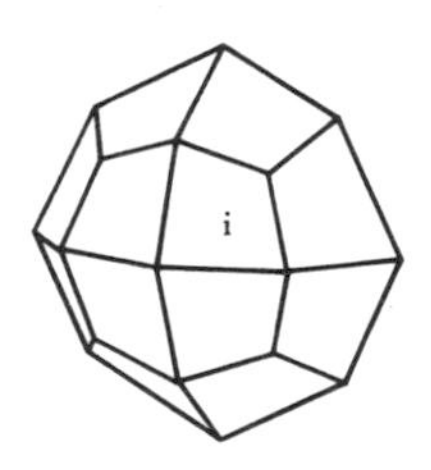

Figure 19: from cube to icositetrahedron (faces *c* and *i* respectively)

Figure 26: hexagonal prism; cross-section of hexagonal prisms and pyramids of I, II, III order

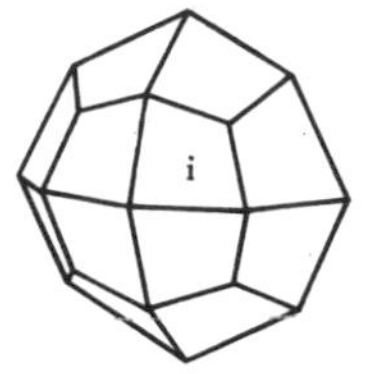

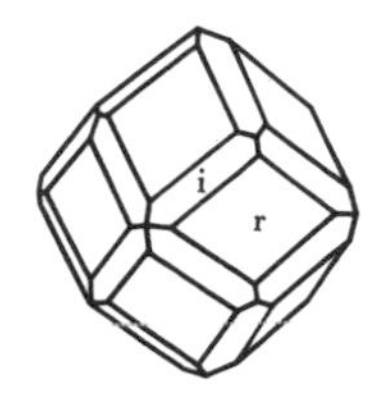

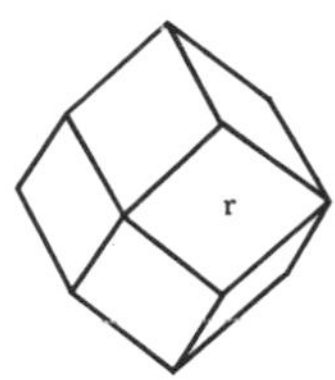

Figure 20: from icositetrahedron to rhombic dodecahedron (faces *i* and *r* respectively)

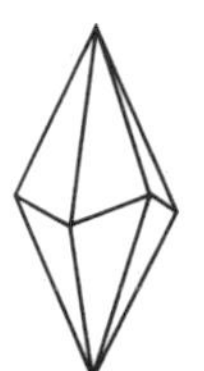
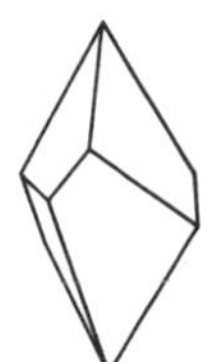

Figure 27: trigonal scalenohedron
Figure 28: trigonal trapezohedron

Figure 21: hexakisoctahedron

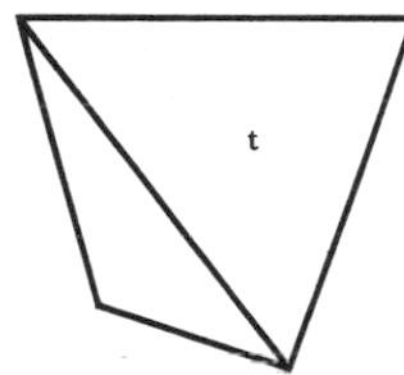

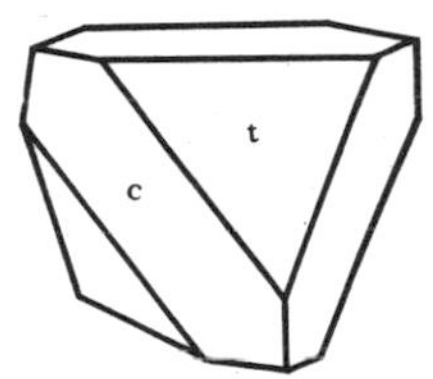

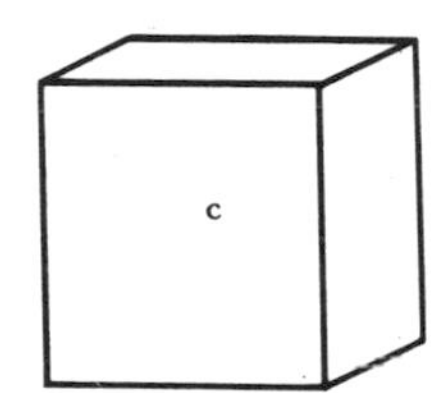

Figure 22: from tetrahedron to cube (faces *t* and *c* respectively)

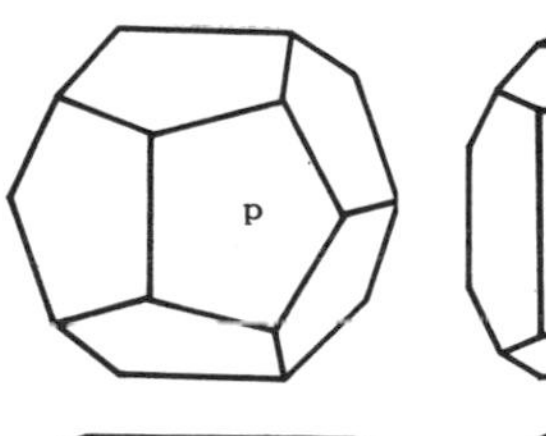

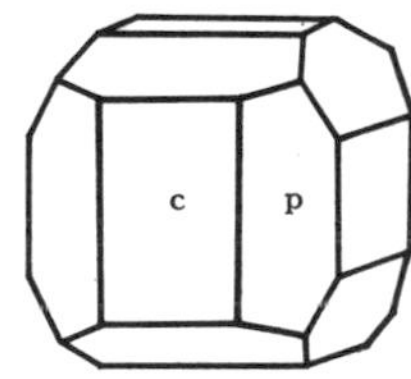

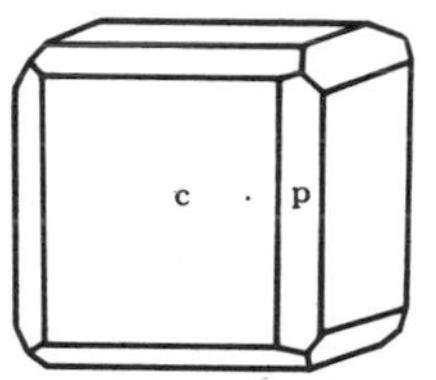

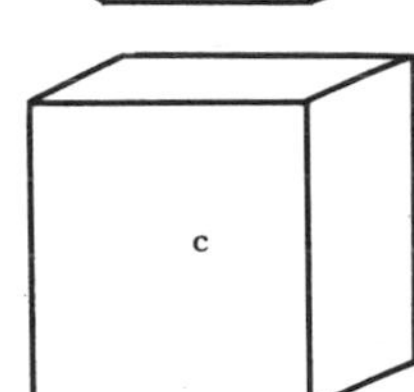

Figure 23: from pentagonal dodecahedron to cube (faces *p* and *c*)

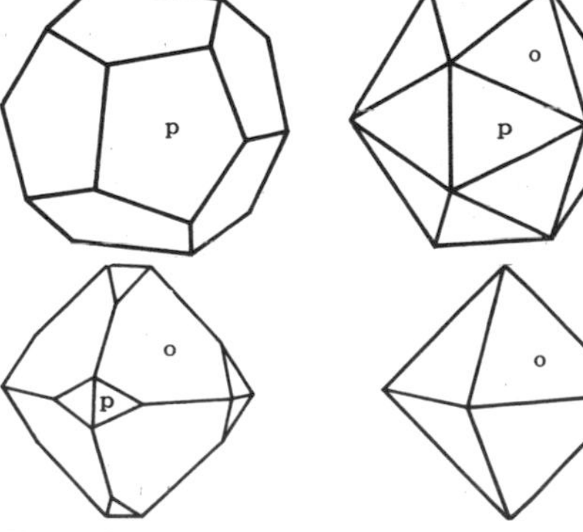

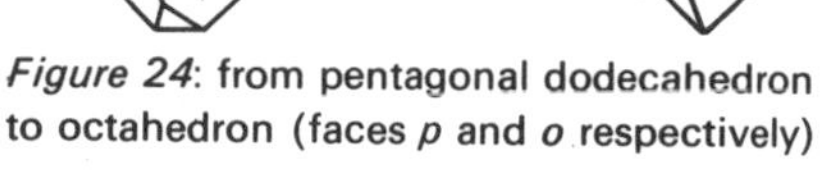

Figure 24: from pentagonal dodecahedron to octahedron (faces *p* and *o* respectively)

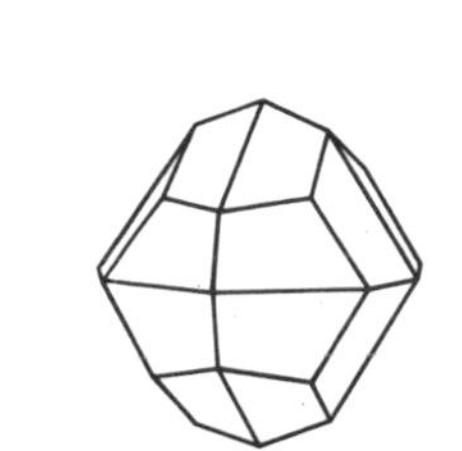

Figure 25: diakisdodecahedron

figures 17 to 25, are the cube, the octahedron, the rhombic dodecahedron, the icositetrahedron, the hexakisoctahedron, the hexakistetrahedron, the triakisoctahedron, the tetrahedron, the pentagonal dodecahedron or pyritohedron, and the diakisdodecahedron or diploid. About 12 per cent of known minerals crystallise in this system, including copper, gold, silver, galena, argentite, fluorite, rock salt, magnetite, analcite, leucite, garnet, uraninite (pitchblende), zinc blende, tetrahedrite, pyrite, hauerite, smaltite, cuprite, sylvine and ullmannite.

HEXAGONAL SYSTEM. As has been pointed out above, the Miller indices for this system are four in number, because of the four crystallographic axes. The class of highest symmetry has one hexad axis, six diad axes, seven planes and a centre of symmetry, and the system can include both closed and open forms. Among the open forms are prisms and pyramids, which can belong to three different orders according to their orientation with respect to the axes; among the closed forms we may mention the bipyramid, the scalenohedron, and the hexagonal trapezohedron. About 8 per cent of known minerals crystallise in this system, notably beryl, pyrrhotite, covellite, molybdenite, apatite, pyromorphite, mimetite, vanadinite, and nepheline.

TRIGONAL SYSTEM. The highest symmetry in this system comprises a triad axis, three diad axes, three planes and a centre of symmetry; as in the hexagonal system there are four crystallographic axes, and consequently four Miller indices. The most characteristic forms are the rhombohedron, the scalenohedron, the hexagonal prism, the trapezohedron and the pyramid. Nearly 9 per cent of minerals crystallise in this system, including: corundum, brucite, hematite, calcite, siderite, smithsonite, rhodochrosite, chabazite, tourmaline, pyrargyrite, millerite, proustite, dolomite, ankerite, dioptase, ilmenite, benitoite, magnesite, quartz and cinnabar.

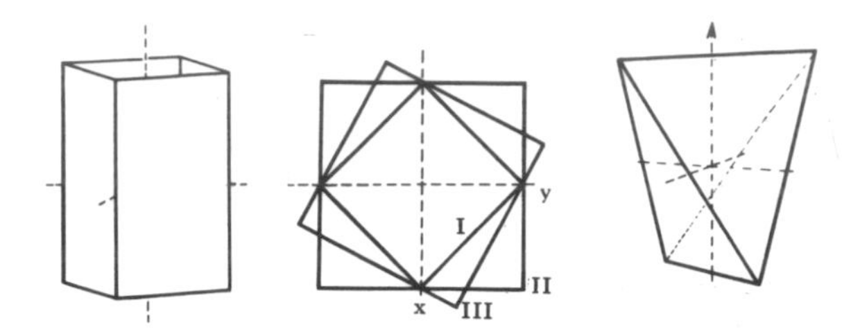

Figure 29: tetragonal prism; cross-sections of prisms and pyramids of various orders; tetragonal bispheoid

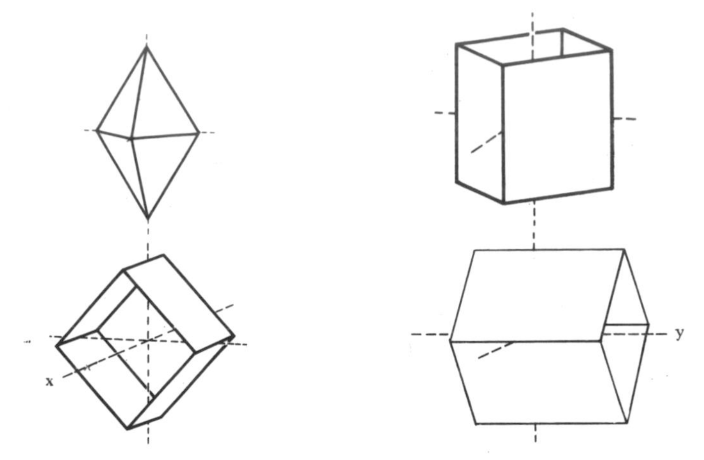

Figure 30: orthorhombic bipyramid; vertical orthorhombic prism; orthorhombic prism parallel to x; orthorhombic prism parallel to y

TETRAGONAL SYSTEM. In this system the highest degree of symmetry comprises a tetrad axis, four diad axes, five planes and a centre of symmetry; it includes prisms of different orders according to their orientation, bipyramids, scalenohedrons, trapezohedrons and sphenoids. Some 10 per cent of minerals crystallise in this system; among others cassiterite, rutile, anatase, torbernite, autunite, zircon, vesuvianite, scheelite, scapolite, phosgenite, wulfenite, chalcopyrite, and gehlenite.

ORTHORHOMBIC SYSTEM. The greatest possible number of elements of symmetry in this system is three diad axes (corresponding with the crystallographic axes), three planes at right angles to each of the axes, and a centre of symmetry. Minerals crystallising in this system, comprising some 22 per cent of known minerals, have rhombic-shaped cross-sections, perpendicular to the length. The most common simple forms are the bipyramid, prisms parallel to the three axes, and the pinacoids. Crystals include those of sulphur, stibnite, bismuthite, arsenopyrite, marcasite, aragonite, strontianite, witherite, sillimanite, andalusite, danburite, topaz, olivine, cordierite, enargite, chalcocite, bournonite, hemimorphite, and aurichalcite.

MONOCLINIC SYSTEM. The highest possible symmetry comprises a diad axis (coinciding with the *y*-axis), a plane perpendicular to this axis, and a centre of symmetry; and these elements allow only prisms and pinacoids. Nevertheless, the largest proportion – some 32 per cent – of minerals belong in this system. Among the more important are wolframite, azurite, malachite, colemanite, gypsum, crocoite, brazilianite, monazite, vivianite, erythrite, sphene (titanite), datolite, epidote, many amphiboles and pyroxenes, orthoclase, heulandite, stilbite, and laumontite.

TRICLINIC SYSTEM. Since the holosymmetric class of this system has only a centre of symmetry, all fundamental forms will be pinacoidal, and crystals will result from the combination of pinacoids. Only 7 per cent of minerals crystallise in this system, such as wollastonite, rhodonite, axinite, kyanite, microcline and the plagioclases.

Development of crystals

It is very rarely that one finds single crystals; generally they occur in groups which have developed together in rock fissures, on flat surfaces known as druses, or in cavities known as geodes. Sometimes crystals develop together, either in contact or actually interpenetrating one another; the same forms constantly recur, and are characteristic of the mineral. These are known as twins. Minerals in which the crystals are too small to be seen are known as massive.

TWINNING. Twinned crystals consist of two or more either in contact or intergrown in such a way that one half is the image of the other either by reflection in a plane, or by rotation through 180°, 120°, or 90° about an axis. The surface along which the two parts of the twin are in contact is called the composition surface.

The reflection plane of a twin can never be a plane of symmetry; and the twin axis can never be a diad, tetrad or hexad axis. So the greater the symmetry of a lattice, the greater the restriction on the planes or axes which can give rise to twinning. For this reason, more varieties of twinning will occur in the triclinic than in the hexagonal system. Some of the various geometrical relationships which can be observed are exemplified by three common types of twinning: the spinel type, in which the twin axis is perpendicular to a possible crystal face; the Carlsbad type, in which the twin axis lies in the plane of the composition surface; and a complex type in which the twin axis also lies in the composition plane, but is perpendicular to three or more faces.

Among characteristic contact twins there are the knee- or elbow-twins of zircon, cassiterite and rutile, the spinel-

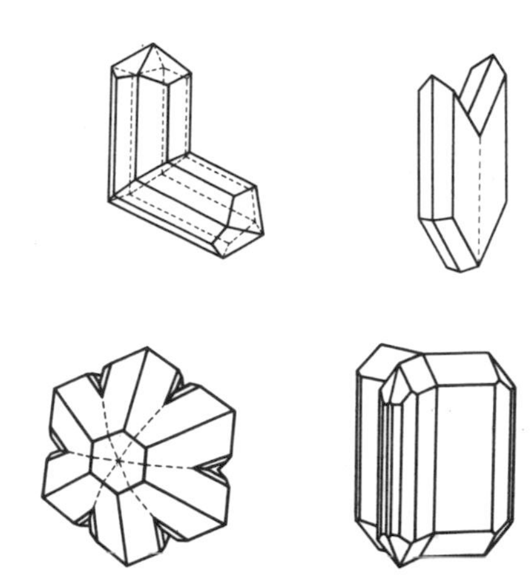

Figure 31: knee-shaped twin of rutile; swallowtail twin of gypsum; chrysoberyl; cerussite

twin, named after this mineral but also occurring in zinc blende, the swallowtail twin of gypsum, and the Manebach and Baveno twins of orthoclase. Among interpenetration twins are the so-called 'Iron Cross' formed by two pentagonal dodecahedra of pyrite, the St Andrew's cross of staurolite (sometimes called the 'fairystone'), and the Carlsbad twin of orthoclase. There are also multiple twins, of which the most common occur in chrysoberyl, rutile, aragonite, cerussite and albite.

AGGREGATES. Most of the minerals that occur in nature are aggregates of imperfect crystals. Because of this a vocabulary has been developed to describe the external and structural features of these aggregates.

The most general of the terms used is *massive*; it can be applied to any mineral without definite crystal form, or composed of masses of small crystals.

Granular means exactly that: the mineral can be seen, either by the naked eye or with a microscope, to have a granular structure. If the grains are visibly coarse, it may be described as *saccharoidal*; a mineral in which the crystal structure is fairly regular, but the individual crystals are too small to be seen, is described as *cryptocrystalline* (sometimes *microcrystalline*). Where the massive mineral has many cleavage faces it is *spathic*.

A mineral has a *columnar* structure when it is composed of slender columns of prisms; when individuals are flattened, as in kyanite, they are said to be *bladed*. Finer structures are *fibrous*. Columnar and fibrous structures may be *reticulate* (like a net), *stellate* (radiating from a centre and producing star-like forms) or *radiate*.

The structure of a mineral is *lamellar* when it comprises plates or leaves; these may be straight or curved. Lamellae may radiate from a common centre and be *concentric*; or they may be *foliated* like mica (the term *micaceous* is sometimes used). *Lenticular* is applied to a particular form of lamellae which are shaped like a lens.

Many specific terms are also used to describe the external appearance of massive minerals – their so-called 'imitative' forms.

Reniform is kidney-shaped; *botryoidal* means consisting of a group of rounded prominences, and is derived from the Greek for a bunch of grapes; *mammillary* is similar to botryoidal, but the prominences are larger; *globular* is spherical, or nearly so. A mineral that is tuberose in shape, or has irregular protuberances on its surface, is described as *nodular*. *Amygdaloidal* means almond-shaped; *coralloidal* is like coral; *dendritic* means branching in a tree-like way. *Mossy* is self-descriptive. *Acicular* means slender and rigid like a needle; *filiform* or *capillary* is very slender and long, like a hair or a thread. *Stalactitic* describes a mineral formed by the percolation of water through cracks; stalactites may be pendant columns, cylinders, or long and irregularly shaped cones.

REGULAR GROWTH OF CRYSTALS. Crystals may grow together in a group in which several features may show regularity; for instance, two or more crystals of the same species may develop in association while maintaining parallelism of one or more of their crystallographic axes, and this is known as parallel grouping. This can also occur with unlike species: quartz and tourmaline may develop together with their triad axes parallel, or rhombohedral calcite may grow on scalenohedral calcite with a triad axis in common. Parallel development can even occur between crystals which have no similarity in chemical composition. Crystals of rutile can grow on tabular crystals of hematite, the vertical axes of the rutile conforming with the horizontal axes of the hematite; or quartz and albite can develop on orthoclase. This is known as orientated development.

Sometimes in a group of crystals it can be seen that each shows a regular and progressive variation in the direction of one or more axes with respect to the preceding individual; this is known as helicoidal development, because the group appears to have been subjected to some torsional force. A regular variation in the direction of the triad axis of the rhombohedral sub-individuals of dolomite produces a saddle shape.

Note on the scale of the photographs
Very few of these photographs are reproduced at a scale of 1:1. For this reason, the size of the longest visible side of each crystal is given in millimetres. In the captions, every crystal is given the system to which it belongs, the locality of origin of the specimen, its size, and a brief commentary on the mineral. In certain cases, a diagram is appended to show the relationships between faces and the combinations of forms.

4 5

1 Cubic system. The variety of grossular garnet known as hessonite. Val d'Ala, Piedmont, Italy (4 mm). The rhombic-shaped face in the centre is part of a rhombic dodecahedron, while the surrounding faces are those of an icositetrahedron. Also noteworthy are the neighbouring prismatic green crystals of diopside and the lamellae of chlorite.

2–4 Cubic system. The pure cube is one of the most characteristic forms of this system, and is exemplified very well in the crystals of galena on dolomite, from Joplin, Missouri, plate 2 (20 mm) and in the excellent specimen of fluorite from Durham, England, plate 3 (13 mm). In Sardinian galena, plate 4 (10 mm) we can see the emergence of the octahedral form.

5–6 Cubic system. The natural occurrence of the octahedral form in fluorite, as in this specimen of pink fluorspar with laumontite from Val d'Ossola, Piedmont (8, 9 mm), is rather rare; on the other hand, cleavage of a shapeless piece of the mineral always yields an octahedron, plate 5 (72 mm).

7 Cubic systems. Fluorite from Eisleben, Saxony (20 mm). The formation of interpenetrant twins, as in this specimen, is common in fluorite.

6 7

8

8 Cubic system. Almandine garnet from Austria (10 mm). The rhombic dodecahedron shown here is the most widely found among the garnets.

9 Cubic system. An icositetrahedral crystal of leucite, from Ariccia, near Rome (9 mm). Note the symmetrical positioning of the two small dark crystals of melanite on the faces of the leucite. The icositetrahedron has also be called the 'leucitohedron', and is the characteristic form of this mineral.

10 Cubic system. Magnetite from Binnatal, Switzerlan (7 mm). Octahedral forms of this mineral are of commo occurrence among the schists of the Alps.

9

10

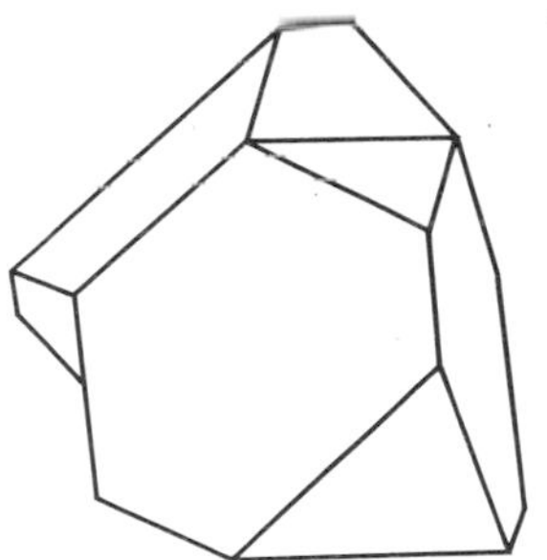

12

1 Cubic system. A copper mineral known as
trahedrite, because it frequently occurs in this habit.
nis specimen, from the Harz district of Germany
7 mm), is covered with a layer of chalcopyrite, and
in the form of a triakistetrahedron.

2 Cubic system. Zinc blende from Switzerland
mm). This is a particular type of twinned crystal,
nown as a 'spinel type', formed by the interpenetration
two crystals made up of two octahedra, as shown in
e diagram.

14

13 Cubic system. Pyrite from Grosseto, Italy (10 mm). The pentagonal dodecahedral form of this mineral is so well known and widespread that it has been given the name of 'pyritohedron'.

14 Cubic system. A fine specimen of pyrite from the island of Elba (9 mm). This mineral occurs in a great variety of forms: visible in the illustration are a cube (the striated faces), an octahedron (appearing as the triangular facet), and a diakisdodecahedron (revealed as the three rhombic faces surrounding this triangular facet).

15

16

15 Cubic system. Another example of pyrite from Elba (14 mm). This specimen is a twinned crystal resulting from the inter-penetration of two pentagonal dodecahedra. Of common occurrence, this crystal is popularly known as the 'Iron Cross'.

16 Cubic system. Hauerite, a manganese sulphide named after Franz Ritter von Hauer. This specimen, from the Destricella mine in Sicily (7 mm), has a combination of forms typical of this system: a cube and an octahedron.

17 Cubic system. Cuprite from Cornwall, England (5 mm), showing the parallel growth of many octahedra.

17

18

19

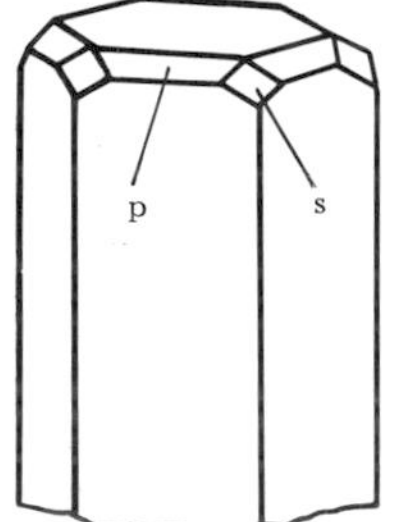

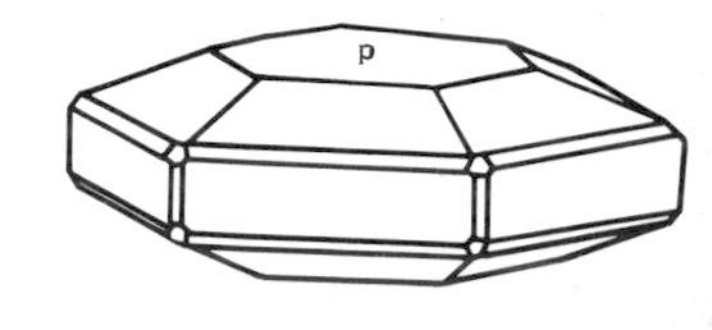

20

18 Hexagonal system. Crystal of pink beryl (morganite) from the island of Elba (9 mm). Associated with the well-developed prism form are two bipyramids, respectively of first order (*p*) and second order (*s*).

19 Hexagonal system. A specimen of Italian apatite (10 mm). Here again the tabular habit should be noted, in which the pinacoid (*p*), facing the observer in the photograph, has developed to a much greater extent than the prism or dipyramid forms.

20 Hexagonal system. Pyrrhotite from Val d'Ossola, Piedmont (4 mm). A mass of tabular crystals in which the pinacoid form is more developed than the prism.

21

22

23

21 Hexagonal system. Mexican apatite (44 mm). This crystal shows both prismatic and dipyramidal forms, but since the former is predominant the habit would be described as prismatic.

22 Hexagonal system. Pyromorphite from Bohemia (8 mm). This occurs principally in a prismatic form, but note the slightly pointed appearance of the ends of the crystal.

23 Hexagonal system. Mimetite, so-called from its resemblance to pyromorphite. This specimen is from Saxony (6 mm). The crystal combines the prism, dipyramid and pinacoid forms.

24 Hexagonal system. Vanadinite from Morocco (3 mm). Crystals are shortest along the prism axis, giving rise to a tabular habit, seen in the upper crystal; below, a nearly perfect hexagonal cross-section.

25 Trigonal system. Sapphire, the blue form of corundum, from Ratnapura, Ceylon (40 mm). The tapering dipyramidal form is characteristic of this mineral, from which the gemstone is cut.

26 Trigonal system. Hematite, a characteristic mineral of the island of Elba (18 mm). Like pyrite, hematite occurs in a wide variety of forms: the upper part of the crystal belongs to a flattened rhombohedron, the other faces to a bipyramid (*n*) and two rhombohedra (*r*, −*r*).

25

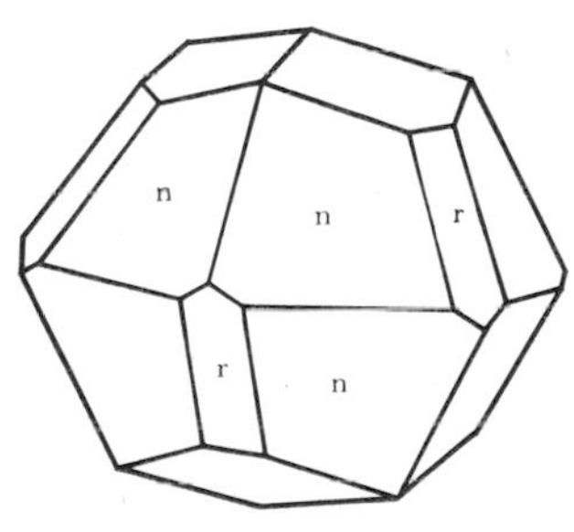

26

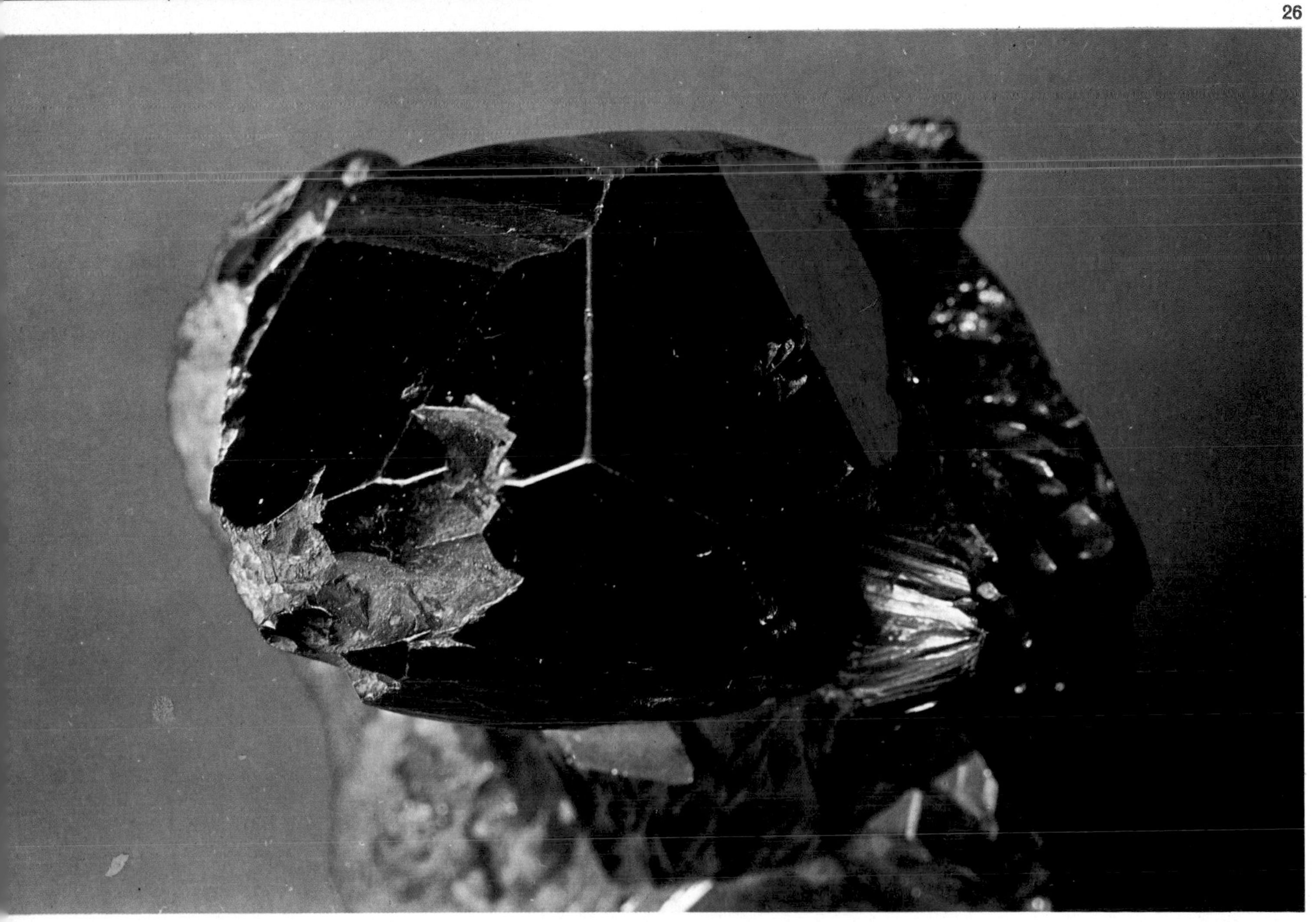

27 Trigonal system. Lamellar hematite with rutile, from Switzerland (40 mm). Note the triangular striations of the hematite.

28 Trigonal system. Rhombohedral crystals of calcite, from Bologna, Italy (10 mm). The shape of the crystals is very close to the form obtained by cleavage.

9

30

29 Trigonal system. Calcite from Cumberland, England (38 mm). This mineral occurs in a wide variety of forms; here we can see the prismatic habit, and the rhombohedral tip. Notice in the interior of the crystal, the fine traces of the cleavage planes, parallel to the fundamental rhombohedron.

30 Trigonal system. A rare form of twinned calcite known as 'Derbyshire type', although this particular specimen comes from Cumberland (25 mm). The composition plane, which is identified by its symmetry, combines two individuals rich in a variety of forms, among which the prism, the scalenohedron and the rhombohedron are predominant. Note also, particularly in the lower part of the crystal, the traces of cleavage planes.

31 Trigonal system. Calcite from Bisuschio, Italy (18 mm). A fine example of an obtuse rhombohedron. Theoretically, the triad axis emerges from the apex in the centre; in plate 29 it is parallel to the edges of the crystal.

31

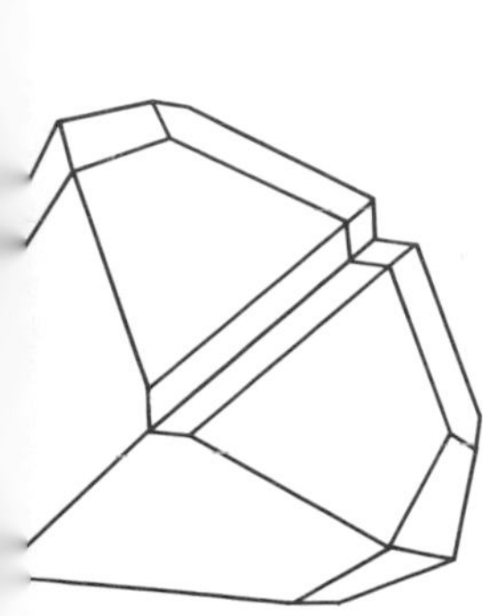

33

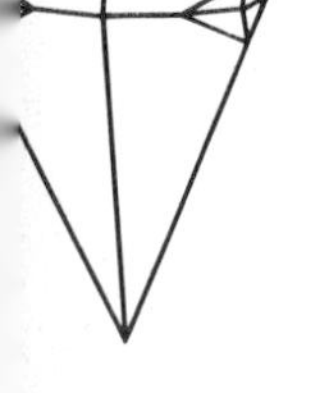

Trigonal system. Twinned crystals of calcite from Derbyshire, England (52 mm). e photograph shows clearly two interpenetrant scalenohedra. This type of twinning quite frequent in calcite.

33 Trigonal system. An example of Italian quartz (85 mm). The habit of this crystal is prismatic with a bipyramid; but one should not identify the pyramid with the top of this specimen. It is, on the contrary, made up of two rhombohedra, a fact which reveals the diversity of the development of faces. The prismatic faces are lightly marked with horizontal striations.

34 Trigonal system. Quartz from Piedmont (195 mm). The pyramidal appearance of much of the quartz from the Alps has given the name 'alpine habit' to this type of crystal.

34

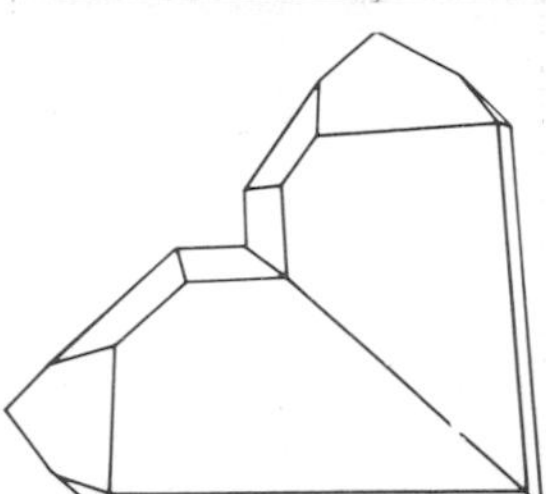

35 Trigonal system. Twinned quartz, from Otomezaka, Japan (30 mm). The two individuals, of a flattened prismatic habit, forr an angle of nearly 90° between them, and meet along the plane parallel to the trigonal bipyramidal face. Contact twins of this kind are rare in quartz, but this, known as the Japanese twin, is perhaps the most familiar. Note the striations which help to identify the faces of the prisms.

36 Trigonal system. Tourmaline from Madagascar (40 mm). This is the end of the crystal, viewed in such a way that the triad symmetry axis emerges from the apex directly toward the observer. The faces belong to two different pyramids.

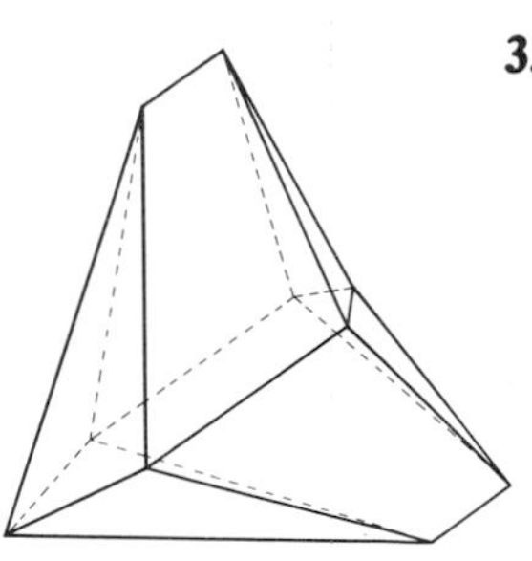

37 Trigonal system. Dolomite, together with quartz and hematite, from near Turin, Italy (35 mm). This is a large rhombohedron of almost perfect shape, in which the cleavage planes are clearly visible.

38 Trigonal system. Ankerite from Bolzano, Italy (20 mm): two rhombohedra forming an interpenetrant twin.

39 Trigonal system. Another calcite twin, from Cumberland (18 mm). From its shape, it has been called a 'butterfly twin', and it is made up of two scalenohedra in contact along a plane whose symmetry is clearly evident. In the foreground can be seen numerous prismatic crystals.

8

9

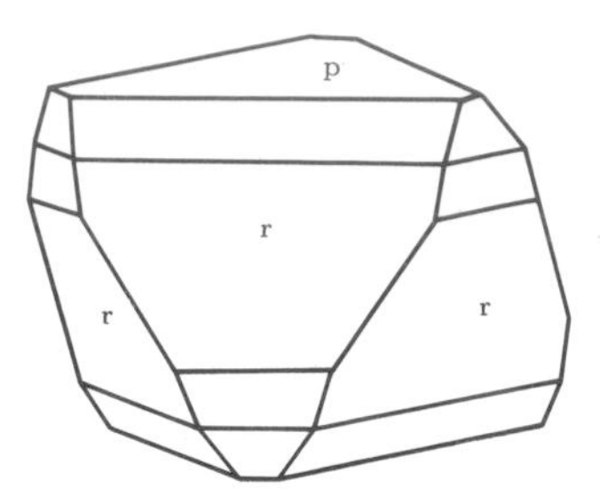

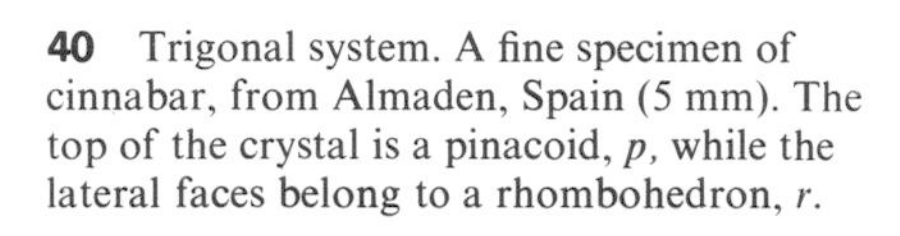
40 Trigonal system. A fine specimen of cinnabar, from Almaden, Spain (5 mm). The top of the crystal is a pinacoid, *p*, while the lateral faces belong to a rhombohedron, *r*.

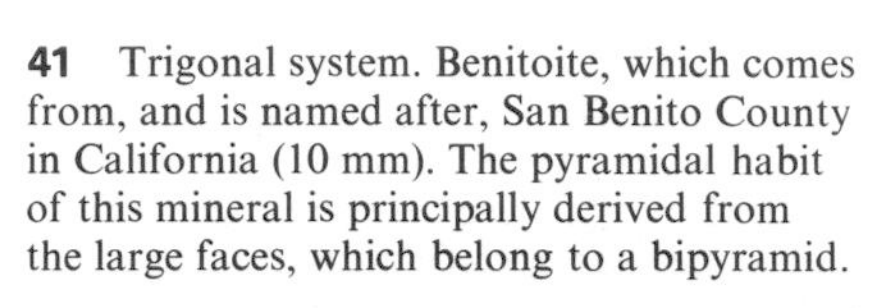
41 Trigonal system. Benitoite, which comes from, and is named after, San Benito County in California (10 mm). The pyramidal habit of this mineral is principally derived from the large faces, which belong to a bipyramid.

2 Tetragonal system. Cassiterite from Brittany, France (18 mm). This specimen has a prismatic habit; notice the faces belonging o two different prisms. The lateral, striated, faces belong to a prism of the first order; the second order prism provides the central dge; while the top of the crystal is pyramidal.

42

43 Tetragonal system. Anatase is also known as 'octahedrite' because its crystals occur in what appears to be this form, although it is in fact a bipyramid. This specimen (5 mm) is from le Bourg-d'Oisans, Dauphiné, France.

44–6 Tetragonal system. Phosgenite from Monteponi, Sardinia. The specimen in plate 44 (60 mm) is a fine example of the prismatic form of this mineral; the well-developed prism is surmounted probably by a trapezohedron, and topped by a pyramid. Plate 45 (22 mm) is of the same mineral from the same locality. One can see the vertical faces of several prisms, the oblique facets of a pyramid, and the horizontal terminal face of a pinacoid. In plate 46 (15 mm), phosgenite is seen in its tabular habit, formed from a short prism and a pinacoid.

45

46

50

47–9 Tetragonal system. Three forms of wulfenite. Plate 47 (9 mm) and plate 49 (7 mm) show crystals from the Old Yuma mine in Arizona. The first, the most widely distributed form, is of tabular habit; as can be seen, the principle face is a basal pinacoid, from the centre of which, and pointing toward the viewer, the tetrad symmetry axis emerges. The lateral faces of two bipyramids should be noted. The second specimen is pseudocubic, being in fact prismatic closed with a pinacoid. Plate 48 (5mm) shows bipyramidal crystals of wulfenite from Carinthia, Austria.

50 Tetragonal system. An association of chalcopyrite with marmatite, the iron-bearing zinc blende, from the Italian Alps (12 mm). Chalcopyrite appears to crystallise in tetrahedra of the cubic system; they are in fact tetragonal bisphenoids.

51 52

53

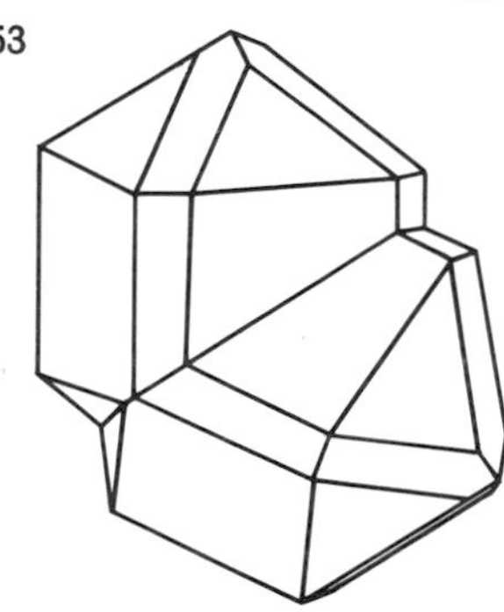

51 Tetragonal system. A twinned crystal of the tin ore cassiterite, from the Schlaggenwald in Bohemia (11 mm). The characteristic re-entrant angle between th two prismatic crystals has given this type of twin the name of 'tin beak'. This re-entrant angle, seen at lower left in the diagram, faces the observer in the photograph.

52 Tetragonal system. Vesuvianite, from Ariccia, near Rome (20 mm). As can be seen, this crystal is a prismatic form topped with a bipyramid.

53 Tetragonal systems. Torbernite from Bois Noir, France (1 mm). These crystals are tabular and considerably flattened; the square section is characteristic of this system, and is an aid in distinguishing these crystals from prismatic crystals of the orthorhombic system, which are rhombic in section.

54 Orthorhombic system. Sicilian sulphur (37 mm). The photograph shows the parallel association of a number of individuals of bipyramidal habit.

55

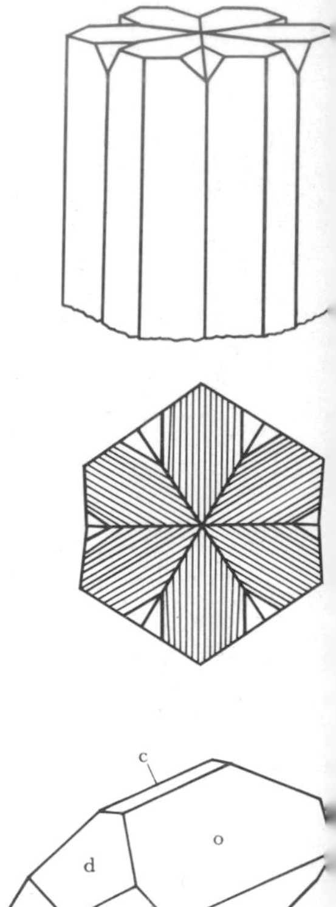

55 Orthorhombic system. Twinned aragonite from Agrigento, Sicily (5 mm). The hexagonal shape of the crystals is due in fact to the interpenetration of three individuals, which appear to give a higher degree of symmetry. The component crystals can be identified by their striations (more easily visible in the diagram right), which are aligned in three different directions.

56 Orthorhombic system. Barite (or barytes) from Piacenza, Italy (18 mm). The prismatic habit of this crystal is determined by the presence of three prisms and a pinacoid. The latter is represented by the tallest vertical face in the centre; to the left of this is a vertical prism *o*, and above, with inclined faces, the two horizontal prisms *d* and *m* (strictly speaking, the prism *m* is vertical, and *d* and *o* horizontal, as shown in the diagram bottom right).

57 Orthorhombic system. Cerussite from Monteponi, Sardinia (24 mm). One can see that the crystal is essentially tabular and derived from a lateral pinacoid; the vertical face at the left is derived from a prism.

56

5

58

59

60

61

58–9 Orthorhombic system. Bournonite from Bohemia. In plate 58 (4 mm), the characteristic tabular form of this rather rare mineral shows how the pinacoid is developed far more than the prismatic faces of the crystal. Illustrated in plate 59 is a twinned crystal (5 mm); the way in which this twin is formed is shown in the diagram below. The pinacoid face is toward the observer.

60 Orthorhombic system. A different form of anglesite from the same mine as the previous specimen (46 mm). The tabular habit is due to the large size of the pinacoid combined with the smallness of the prisms making up the edges of the crystal.

61 Orthorhombic system. The characteristic form of anglesite; these crystals are from Sardinia (25 mm). The cleavage planes which follow the prismatic top to the crystal are clearly visible. Anglesite (lead sulphate) and cerussite (lead carbonate), which are frequently found together in mineral deposits of lead and zinc, occur in forms and combinations that are almost identical; but they can be readily distinguished by chemical analysis.

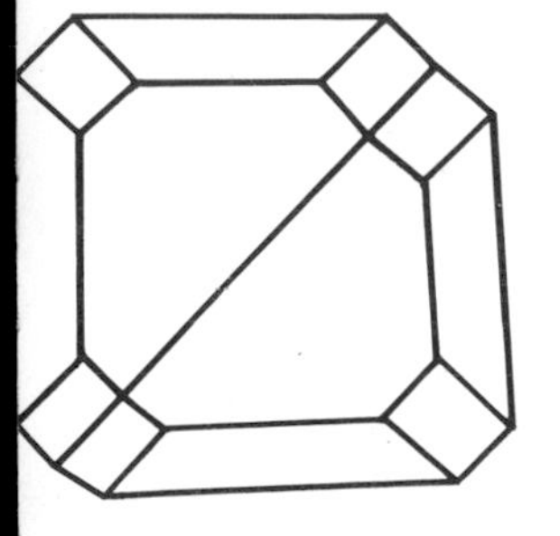

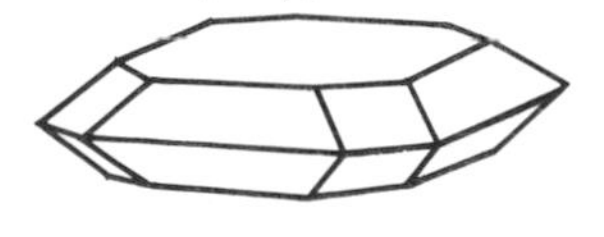

62

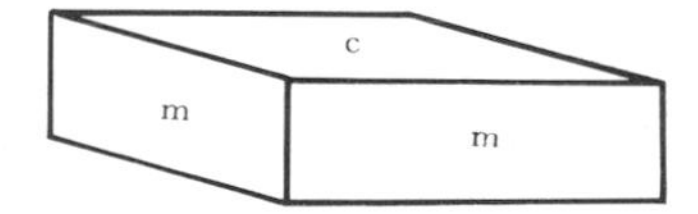

62–3 Orthorhombic system. Plate 70 shows a tabular form of barite, from near Turin, Italy (20 mm). Here the pinacoid forms the largest face, while the lateral faces are of the prism *m*. When these faces become particularly small the crystal reaches a lamellar habit, as shown in plate 71, which comes from a mine in Sardinia (25 mm). The face toward the observer is the pinacoid, from which the crystallographic *z* axis emerges.

64 Orthorhombic system. Danburite from San Luis Potosi, Mexico (55 mm). Here again, the typical forms of the orthorhombic system, already observed in barite and anglesite, can be seen.

63

64

67

65 Monoclinic system. Azurite from Tsumeb, South-West Africa (10 mm). These crystals, which are prismatic in form, are partly covered with malachite.

66 Monoclinic system. Epidote, from Pinzgau, Austria (26 mm). An aggregate of prismatic individuals; the longest faces are pinacoids, while the shortest belong to a prism.

67 Monoclinic system. Gypsum from Wiesloch, Germany (40 mm). A combination of the most common forms of this mineral is shown here: pinacoid, to the left; vertical prism, the two faces toward the observer; and oblique prism, the two faces at the top of the crystal.

69 70

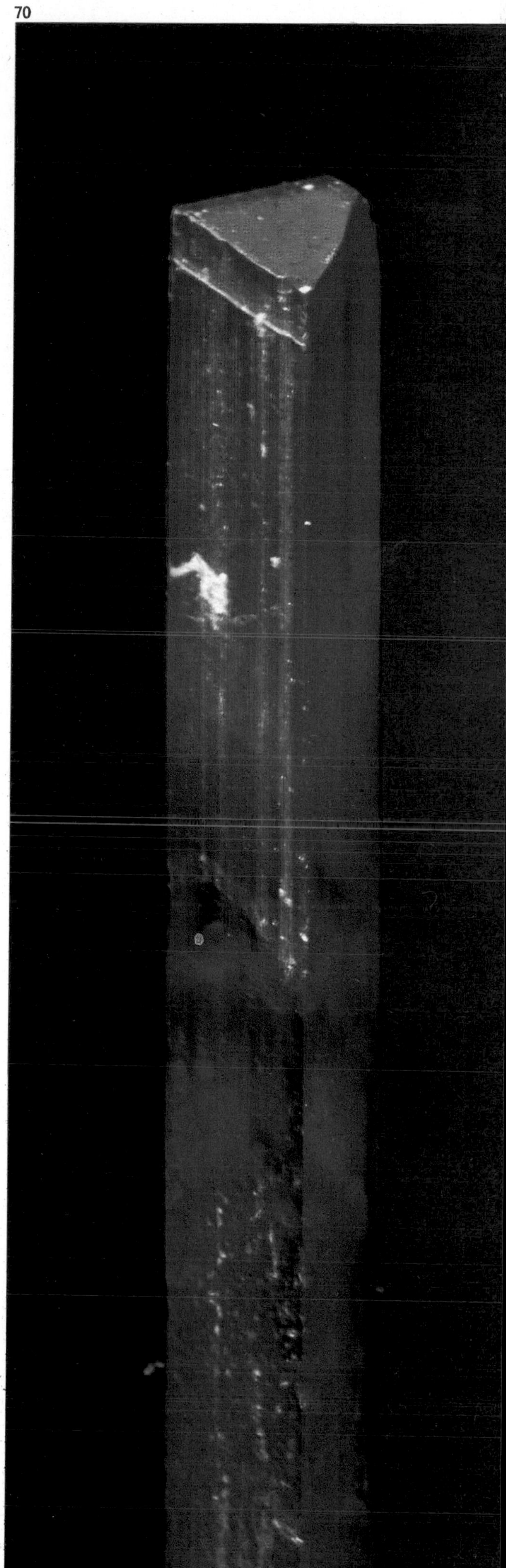

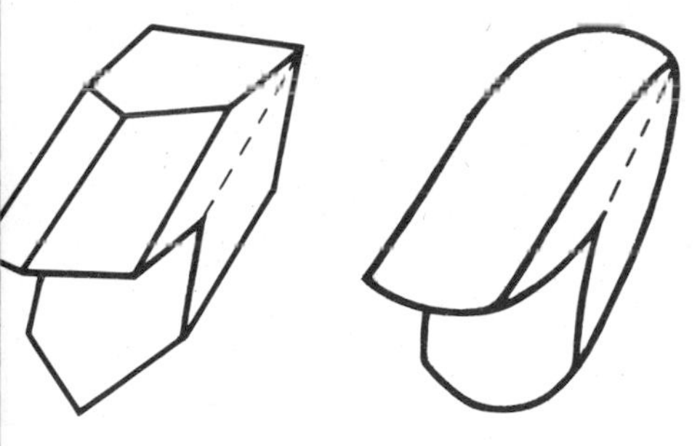

8 Monoclinic system. Twinned gypsum from the Gallitano mine in Italy (180 mm). This type of vin is called 'spearhead' or 'arrowhead' because of its shape; the composition plane is also a plane f symmetry for the two individuals.

9 Monoclinic system. Titanite from Bolzano, Italy (7 mm). Alternatively known as sphene (from ne Greek for 'wedge'), this mineral is frequently found twinned. The form is fairly simple, and milar to a rhombohedron: two faces belong to a prism, the third is a pinacoid.

0 Monoclinic system. Crocoite from Dundas, Tasmania (26 mm). This crystal, of prismatic habit nd of remarkable length, is closed at the top with the face of an oblique prism. The inclination of ne top edge is characteristic of this system.

71

71 Monoclinic system. Orthoclase from the island of Elba (25 mm). Thi variety of orthoclase is called 'sanidine' from the Greek for 'board', because of its tabular habit, which is due to the large pinacoid face. The two near faces belong to a prism; those above and below belong to other pinacoids.

72 Monoclinic system. Adularia, another variety of orthoclase, from th Italian Alps (26 mm). This translucent, sometimes transparent, feldspar is quite common in the Alps; it is characterised by the presence of only one prism *m* and a single pinacoid, *x* or *c*, arranged in such a way as to resemble a calcite rhombohedron (see diagram, left).

73 Monoclinic system. Another variety of orthoclase twin, known as a Baveno twin, after the district of Lake Maggiore, Piedmont, from which this specimen comes (53 mm). The crystals here have a prismatic appearance, but the largest faces belong to a pinacoid, the prism being reduced to the terminal faces. The contact plane is clearly visible in the photograph, as is the face of the vertical prism *m* turned toward the observer (diagram, right).

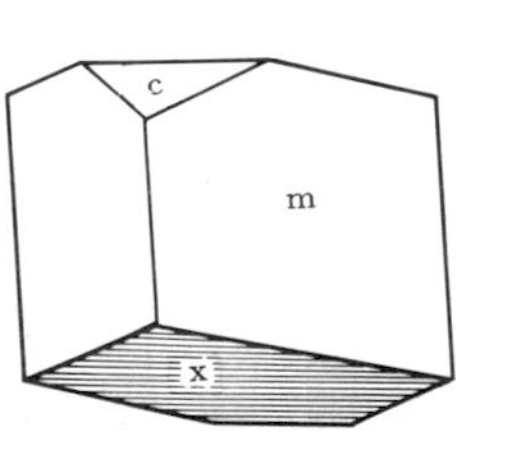

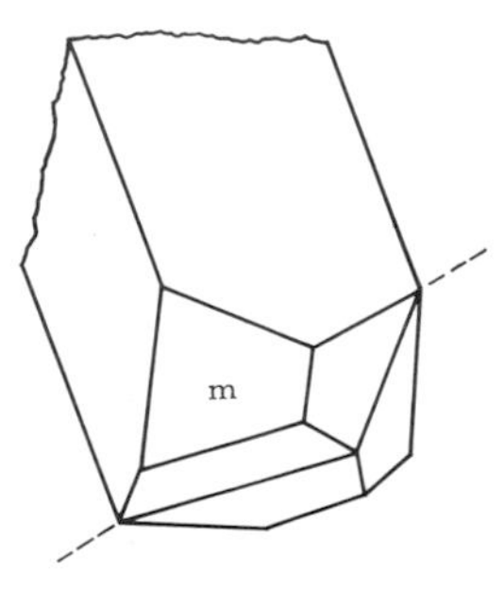

72

74

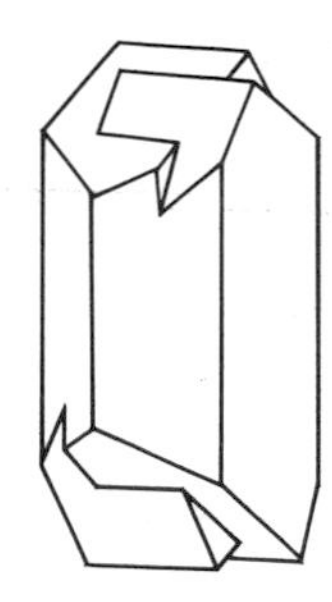

75

4 Monoclinic system. The orthoclase twin known as the Carlsbad type, ıfter the locality in Czechoslovakia where it is commonly found; this pecimen (20 mm) is from Viterbo, Italy. This twin is an interpenetration of wo individuals (in this case of sanidine) along a plane parallel to the inacoid, as shown in the diagram above. This is the most common type of winning in orthoclase crystals.

'5 Monoclinic system. Stilbite from the Faroe Islands (33 mm). The rystals are in an aggregate of characteristic sheaf-like form, in which the ndividuals are slightly displaced with respect to one another.

76 77

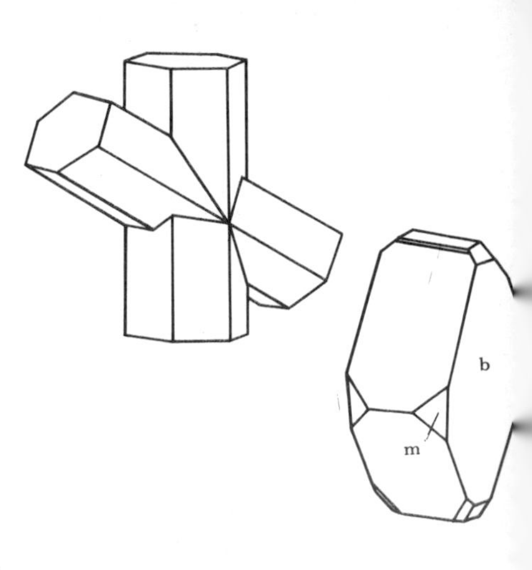

76–7 Monoclinic system. Staurolite from the Italian Alps, plate 76 (37 mm), and its remarkable twinned form, known as cross-stone or fairystone, from Antsirabe, Madagascar (12 mm). From the point of view of geometry this mineral would appear to belong to the orthorhombic system: the slender prismatic form is closed by pinacoid, and the angle β between the x and z axes is very nearly 90°, giving rise to what is known as pseudosymmetry. Staurolite twins are generally interpenetration twins with the two arms at right angles (the name is derived from the Greek for 'cross-stone'), but the 60° angle and the slight skew of the twin in the photograph is due to the twin plane being parallel to a bipyramid face.

78 Monoclinic system. Heulandite from Trento, Italy (8 mm). As the diagram shows, the large face is a pinacoid, *b*, as are the other faces with the exception of *m*, which is that of a prism. The cleavage planes following the pinacoid *b* are clearly visible in the photograph.

78

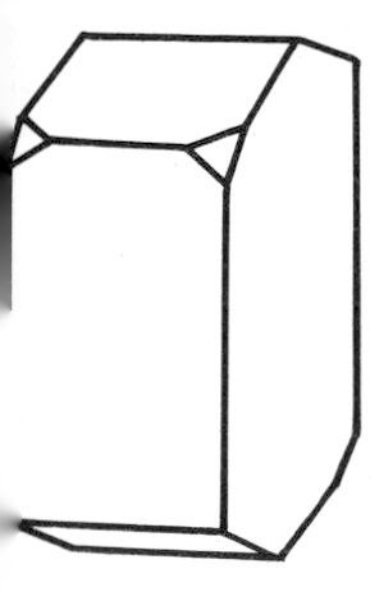

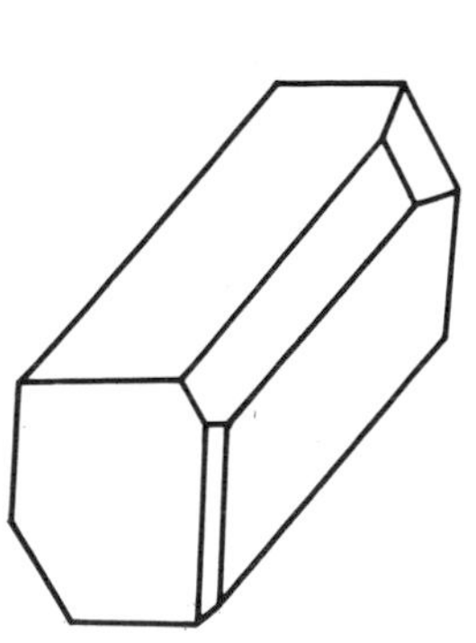

80

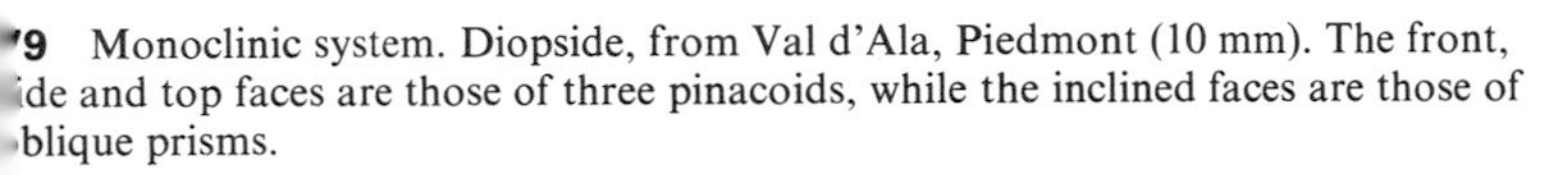

'9 Monoclinic system. Diopside, from Val d'Ala, Piedmont (10 mm). The front, ide and top faces are those of three pinacoids, while the inclined faces are those of blique prisms.

0 Triclinic system. Kyanite from the Italian Alps (55 mm). The crystals of this ineral are always very flattened and micalike, but elongated.

1 Triclinic system. Axinite, from Dauphiné, France (6 mm). Axinite crystals have characteristic appearance, almost as though they are crystals with a higher ymmetry that have been accidentally flattened. As can be seen, triclinic crystals have very low degree of symmetry, and it is difficult to determine their orientation, as ne can with other systems, in the absence of axes or planes of symmetry. In this ase, all the faces are pinacoids.

81

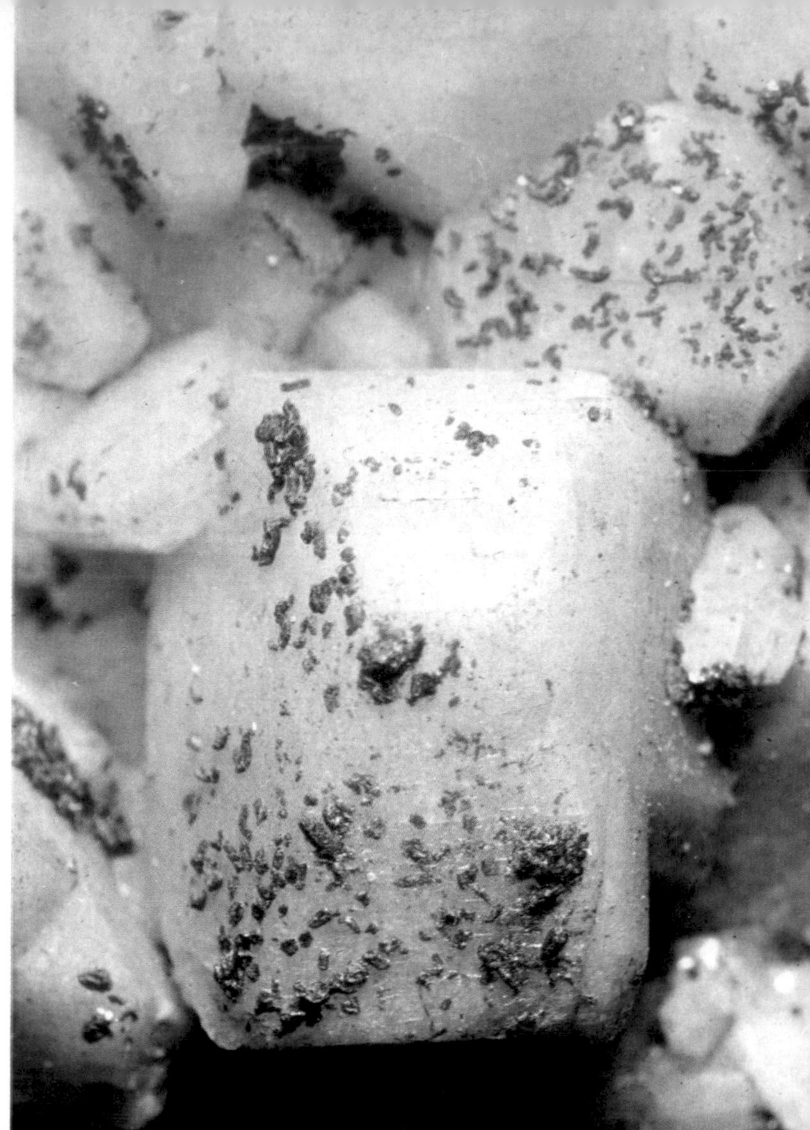

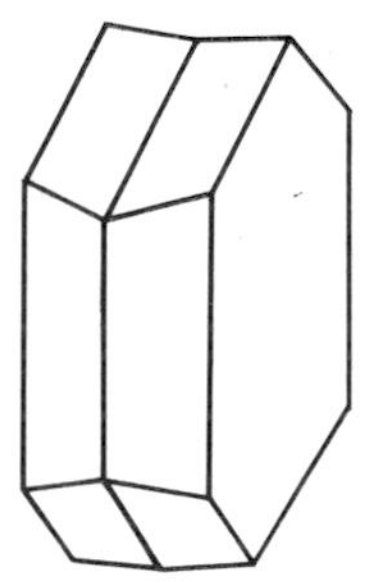

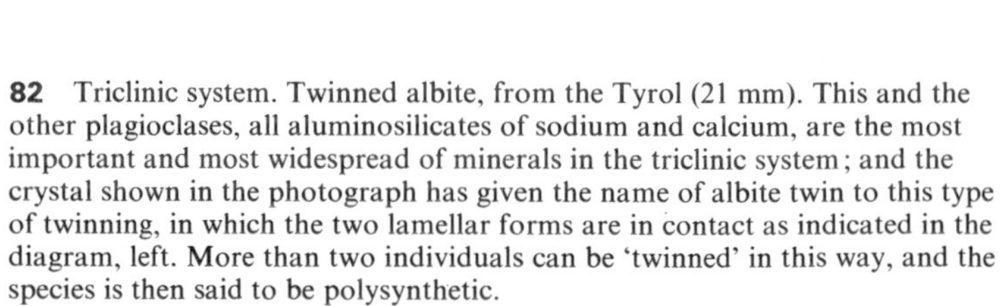

82 Triclinic system. Twinned albite, from the Tyrol (21 mm). This and the other plagioclases, all aluminosilicates of sodium and calcium, are the most important and most widespread of minerals in the triclinic system; and the crystal shown in the photograph has given the name of albite twin to this type of twinning, in which the two lamellar forms are in contact as indicated in the diagram, left. More than two individuals can be 'twinned' in this way, and the species is then said to be polysynthetic.

83 Triclinic system. The pericline variety of albite also forms characteristic twins. This specimen is from Bolzano, Italy (10 mm). The crystal is made up of a number of pinacoids, of which the upper and lower are the most developed, as the diagram, right, shows.

84 A single rod-like crystal of rutile, with quartz crystals, from Tavetsch, Switzerland (30 mm). When the prismatic habit is lengthened in this way, and the crystal is not too fine, it is said to be columnar.

85 A group of prismatic crystals of pyromorphite, from Bohemia (6 mm). The individual crystals have developed in various directions, without any regular alignment.

86 Dioptase from Mindouli, Congo (32 mm radius). This aggregate is radiate-columnar in type; the structure is regular, and the orientation of each individual differs a little from the adjoining ones.

85

86

87

88

87 Plumosite, from the Italian Alps. This aggregate is filamentous, and completely disordered. The individual crystals are very fine and needle-like; together they look like a mass of hairs.

88 Stilbite from Rio Grande do Sul, Brazil (75 mm radius), which occurs in a radiatelamellar aggregate. The individuals can be seen from their lamellar cleavage planes.

89 Wavellite from Devonshire, England (12 mm radius). The globular structure is made up of an aggregate of fibres, radiating from the centre of a spherical body, as can be seen in the cross-sections which are visible.

90 Malachite from the Urals (78 mm). This aggregate is mammillary, characterised by a surface covered with rounded prominences. In section, it is generally found to be made up of several layers, often of different colours with a fibrous structure. This stratified structure is called 'concretionary' or 'concentric'.

89

90

91

92

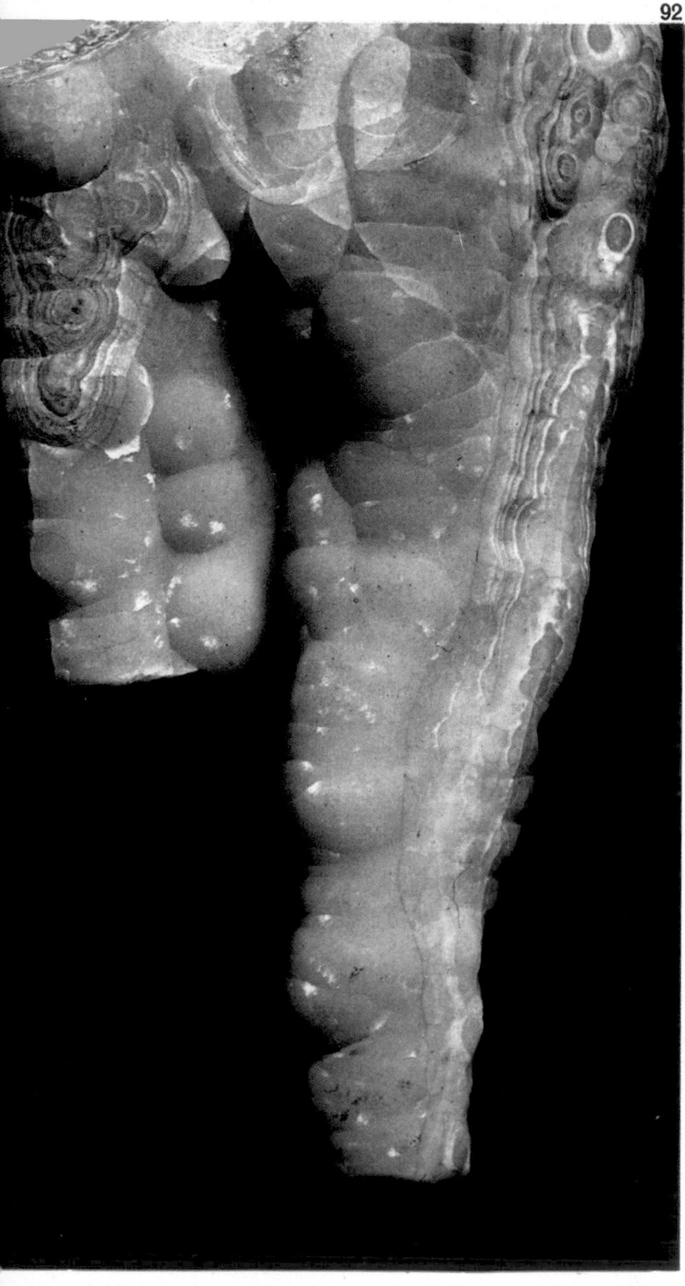

93 94

91 Malachite from Katanga. This type of aggregate is described as botryoidal, from the Greek for a bunch of grapes. The name describes a particular type of rounded forms, not separated from each other but well defined like the individual grapes in a tight bunch. An isolated rounded form is called 'reniform'.

92 Smithsonite from Iglesias, Sardinia (130 mm). This aggregate is known as stalactitic, by analogy with the concretions of calcite which form in caves under the action of dripping water.

93 Native silver from the Harz mountains in Germany (38 mm). This form is called dendritic, from its similarity to the branches of a tree; more strictly, this particular specimen should be described as 'reticular-dendritic', since the forms are crosslinked into a mesh.

94 Aragonite from Styria, Austria, in the form known as coralloid; it is found frequently in the upper levels of iron ore deposits, and is known also as 'flos ferri'.

95

96

7

95–7 Rosette aggregates. Plate 95. Hematite from St Gothard (20 mm diameter). Often lamellar or lenticular crystals of various minerals – such as hematite, pyrrhotite, gypsum, barite – grow in these rose-like forms. Hematite aggregates of this type are known as 'iron roses'. Plate 96. Romanian pyrrhotite (60 mm diameter) with some crystals of zinc blende at the centre. Plate 97. A similar aggregate of gypsum, known as a 'desert rose', since this type of aggregate is formed under arid desert conditions, such as those in the Sahara, from which this specimen comes (80 mm diameter).

98 Parallel development of amethyst, the mauve variety of quartz, from Bolzano, Italy (44 mm). The four individuals all have their various elements (such as the triad axis, which emerges from the upper apex) in parallel alignment.

98

100

99 Another example of parallel development in quartz, from Bologna, Italy (25 mm). On the faces of these small parallel crystals one can see hollow areas, due to more rapid growth along the edges of the crystals. These are called hopper crystals

100 Parallel development in red tourmaline from Antrandkomby, Madagascar (50 mm). As in the case of the quartz, one can see the parallelism of the corresponding crystallographic planes in the two adjoining crystals.

101 Orientated development of quartz on orthoclase (70 mm). The small quartz crystals have orientated themselves with the same directions of growth on the prismatic faces of the orthoclase.

101

102 Helicoidal development in quartz from Oberalp, Switzerland (60 mm). This form is obtained by the association of a number of individual crystals succeeding one another in growth with a regular variation in the inclination of the axis.

103 Saddle-form development in dolomite from Italy. Here the rhombohedra have incurved faces made up of smaller individual crystals slightly displaced in relation to one another.

102

1(